D1642476

A COURSE IN MODERN TECHNIQUES OF
ORGANIC CHEMISTRY

A COURSE IN MODERN TECHNIQUES OF ORGANIC CHEMISTRY

R. P. LINSTEAD, C.B.E., F.R.S.,

J. A. ELVIDGE, Ph.D., A.R.C.S.

and

MARGARET WHALLEY, Ph.D.,

of the

Imperial College of Science and Technology

LONDON

BUTTERWORTHS SCIENTIFIC PUBLICATIONS

1955

BUTTERWORTHS PUBLICATIONS LTD.
88 KINGSWAY, LONDON, W.C. 2

AFRICA: BUTTERWORTH & CO. (AFRICA) LTD.
                 DURBAN: 33/35 Beach Grove
AUSTRALIA: BUTTERWORTH & CO. (AUSTRALIA) LTD.
                 SYDNEY: 8 O'Connell Street
                 MELBOURNE: 430 Bourke Street
                 BRISBANE: 240 Queen Street
CANADA: BUTTERWORTH & CO. (CANADA) LTD.
                 TORONTO: 1367 Danforth Avenue
NEW ZEALAND: BUTTERWORTH & CO. (AUSTRALIA) LTD.
                 WELLINGTON: 49/51 Ballance Street
                 AUCKLAND: 35 High Street

U.S.A. Edition published by
ACADEMIC PRESS INC., PUBLISHERS
125 EAST 23RD STREET
NEW YORK 10, NEW YORK

Set in Monotype Baskerville type

Printed in England by
ADLARD AND SON LIMITED
London and Dorking

INTRODUCTION

THIS book is based on a new course in organic chemistry which was introduced in 1951 at the Imperial College of Science and Technology. The course was designed to meet a growing need in the experimental training of students. We think the need is general although its impact will vary according to the methods of different teaching institutions and the requirements of those who attend them. We have been reinforced in this opinion by discussions with teachers and students from other universities and other countries, and interest in the new course has been so great that it has seemed that it would be useful to make a description available.

The science of organic chemistry was built up during its 'classical' period, say from 1860 to 1930, by the use of a few remarkably simple experimental techniques. It was easy for a student to learn these by carrying out a number of syntheses involving typical reactions and operations; and from analytical work, both qualitative and quantitative. The result was that the average new graduate at B.Sc. level was able to proceed to original laboratory investigation, either pure or applied, with little further formal technical training.

During the last two decades or so, the practice of organic chemistry has been greatly affected by the introduction of powerful new techniques, without which many of the striking advances of recent years would have been impossible. Microanalysis and chromatography will serve as examples. This development, although it greatly strengthened the hands of the research chemist, introduced an educational problem. A gap opened between the experimental training of the average graduate and the requirements of the research worker. In practice this gap has generally been bridged in an *ad hoc* manner by the new research worker learning the particular advanced technique or techniques necessary for the study of his own problems; but as a consequence, his knowledge of other methods remains at the first degree level, which may be very low indeed.

Accordingly, the organized teaching of experimental organic chemistry at the Imperial College of Science and Technology was widened by the introduction of the course in modern techniques which is described in this book. As a matter of organization it

v

forms part of the undergraduate work of the organic chemical specialists at the College in their third (post-intermediate) year, but it is essentially a transitional course and is also taken in part by new research students at graduate level from other institutions.

There are, of course, many admirable books and monographs which go exhaustively into the various contemporary techniques. For example there are standard works on fractional distillation and on chromatography. It is not our purpose to duplicate these. We have selected some twenty nine topics which are treated in short separate chapters. Each chapter outlines, as appropriate, the general basis of the method and gives a description *in exact working detail* of its application in some particular instance. Our objects are, first, to provide instructions which are completely reliable so that the student acquires confidence in the particular technique, and secondly, to illustrate the basic principles involved. We have tried to avoid undue complication in apparatus. Consequently the procedures described, while good, are not necessarily the most recent elaborations since modifications are easily assimilated later if the principles have been properly learned. Each chapter contains a list of key references and suggestions for further reading.

The book is divided into three sections:

Techniques of Separation and Purification
Special Reaction Techniques
Techniques of Quantitative Analysis and Allied Physical Measurements.

It has not always been easy to decide what should be included and what omitted. Our guiding principle has been to include those methods and operations with which a trained organic chemist should be practically familiar and which he should be able to perform for himself. We have *included* a number of comparatively simple topics, for example the final purification and drying of substances for analysis, reactions in Carius tubes, and catalytic hydrogenation at atmospheric pressure, because it is our experience that new research students often fail in these operations. We have *omitted* those operations which in our opinion are best carried out by specially trained technical staff, at least in large research departments or organizations. For this reason there is no mention of determinations of infra-red spectra, of the 'counting' of radioactive material, or of most quantitative microanalytical procedures. All these methods are carried out in this department by specialists on a 'service' basis and instruction to students in their use is by lecture and demonstration, not by practical work. We have, however, *included* the semi-micro determination of carbon and hydrogen, and the full micro determination of nitrogen by the Kjeldahl method, on the grounds of educational usefulness. We have *excluded* one or two of the latest techniques, such as vapour-phase chromatography, because we have not yet had sufficient practical experience with them.

It may be helpful if a few remarks are added on the operation of the course based on these methods. Most of the various pieces of equipment are permanently assembled and used only for the purpose of the course during its running. Each student moves from one set of apparatus to the next. The time occupied is about 200 hours. During this period a good student will have completed satisfactorily some 15–20 exercises. The experimental work is complemented during its early stages with a course of 7 lectures on the general principles involved. Although, as has been said, we have tried to avoid undue elaboration of apparatus, some of the items are necessarily expensive. The total capital cost of the special equipment for the course at the Imperial College of Science and Technology approached £2000.

In preparing this book and devising the experiments which it describes, we have drawn greatly on the special knowledge of many members of this department. We wish to acknowledge in particular the very great help given by Prof. H. N. RYDON in the pioneering stages. Drs L. N. OWEN, E. A. BRAUDE and B. C. L. WEEDON have also given valuable guidance. Of the technical staff we acknowledge particularly the able assistance of R. H. YOUNG and J. A. PEPPERCORN and the advice of F. H. OLIVER on microanalytical procedures. Much valuable experimental help, particularly in adapting the various methods for teaching purposes, was given by Miss J. FILDES, then of the National University of Australia. Finally several helpful suggestions have come from the students of the College who have taken the course. It is a great pleasure to acknowledge our debt to all these and to thank them for their help.

R. P. LINSTEAD
J. A. ELVIDGE
M. WHALLEY

South Kensington   *February, 1955*

NOTES

(1) WHERE elaborate instruments are involved and it is necessary to make the instructions clear, the name of the equipment and of the manufacturers is given. The source of certain chemicals is also specified. This means that these materials are known to be satisfactory for the stated purposes. It has not been possible to examine alternatives so that the recommendations should not be taken to constitute an endorsement of the particular model (or chemical) in comparison with any equivalent made by another manufacturer.

(2) Journal abbreviations conform with those given in the *World List of Scientific Periodicals 1900–1950*, 3rd edn, Butterworths Scientific Publications, London, 1952.

(3) Symbols, signs and abbreviations, except 'm. pt' and 'b. pt', are those recommended for British scientific publications by the Symbols Committee of the Royal Society in *A Report*, The Royal Society, London, 1951.

(4) Throughout the text, temperatures are given in degrees Centigrade.

CONTENTS

CONTENTS

PART III. TECHNIQUES OF QUANTITATIVE ANALYSIS AND ALLIED PHYSICAL MEASUREMENTS

PART I

TECHNIQUES OF PURIFICATION
AND SEPARATION

1
ADSORPTION CHROMATOGRAPHY

INTRODUCTION

CHROMATOGRAPHY is an established technique for the separation of mixtures and for the purification of compounds.

In adsorption chromatography, a solution of the material is run on to a column of adsorbent and solvent is then allowed to percolate through slowly. The chromatogram develops, i.e. the solutes separate in zones or bands down the column in the order of their affinities for the adsorbent. By continued elution, the separated solutes may be washed from the column into the eluate which is collected in separate portions. Alternatively the column may be sucked dry, extruded and divided. The material in the separate zones can then be extracted.

REFERENCES

CASSIDY, *Technique of Organic Chemistry*, Interscience Publishers, Inc., New York, 1951, Vol. V.

LEDERER and LEDERER, *Chromatography*, Elsevier Publishing Company, Amsterdam, 1953.

STRAIN, *Chromatographic Adsorption Analysis*, Interscience Publishers, Inc., New York, 1942.

WILLIAMS, *An Introduction to Chromatography*, Blackie and Son Ltd, London, 1948; *The Elements of Chromatography*, Blackie and Son Ltd, London, 1954, Chapter 2.

ZECHMEISTER and CHOLNOKY, *Principles and Practice of Chromatography*, Chapman and Hall Ltd, London, 1941.

Grading of alumina: BROCKMANN and SCHODDER, *Ber. dtsch. chem. Ges.*, 1941, **74**, 73. An English translation is available from Peter Spence and Sons Ltd, Widnes, Lancashire.

Preparation of aluminas of definite graded adsorptive capacity: pamphlet by Peter Spence and Sons Ltd.

(i) PURIFICATION OF ANTHRACENE. DRY-PACKING OF A COLUMN

The apparatus is shown in *Figure 1.* Push a plug of cotton-wool to the bottom of the tube. Introduce alumina (Savory and Moore, London) (3–4 cm depth), tap the tube with a spatula fairly vigorously about 5 cm above the alumina and press the alumina down

3

firmly with a pestle made from thick glass rod. Introduce and press down further lots of alumina until a column 20 cm long is obtained. Moisten the alumina with *n*-hexane, press the alumina down with the pestle and carefully level off the top of the column

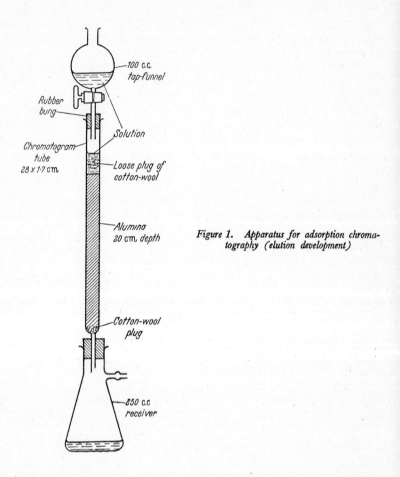

Figure 1. *Apparatus for adsorption chroma-tography (elution development)*

which must now be kept covered with solvent (depth *ca.* 5 cm). Push a loose plug of cotton-wool to within 1 cm of the alumina. From the tap-funnel run in a solution of technical anthracene (50 mg) in *n*-hexane (50 c.c.) and adjust the flow rate to 1–2 drops/second. If necessary, apply gentle suction but avoid evaporating

4

the solvent from the bottom of the column. Develop the chromatogram with *n*-hexane (100 c.c.) and examine the column in ultraviolet light (e.g. from a Hanovia lamp, Hanovia Ltd, Slough); three bands will be seen:

(*a*) Top. Narrow blue fluorescent band (carbazole)

(*b*) Middle. Yellow non-fluorescent band (naphthacene)

(*c*) Bottom. Broad blue-violet fluorescent band (anthracene).

Continue the development with *n*-hexane (*ca.* 75 c.c.). Change the receiver when fluorescent material begins to pass into the eluate. Then elute the anthracene with 1/1 *n*-hexane–benzene, and evaporate the eluate under reduced pressure to give pure anthracene (*ca.* 30 mg), m.pt 213·5°, visibly fluorescent in daylight.

Clean and dry the column and reject the alumina.

(ii) SEPARATION OF 2 : 4-DINITROPHENYLHYDRAZONES.
WET-PACKING OF A COLUMN

The apparatus is shown in *Figure 1*. Clean the tube with hot chromic–sulphuric acid and rinse and dry it. Push a *glass*-wool plug to the lower end. Shake bentonite (British Drug Houses Ltd, Poole) (28 g) with kieselguhr ('acid-washed', British Drug Houses) (7 g) in a 250-c.c. conical flask and slurry the mixture with chloroform (55 c.c.). Swirl the slurry and pour it steadily into the column. Tap the column with the broad side of a ruler whilst the adsorbent settles, so that air bubbles may rise. Rinse down the inside of the column with chloroform: the depth of solvent above the adsorbent should be 5–7 cm. Push a small plug of glass-wool to within 1 cm of the adsorbent, and, when the solvent level has fallen nearly to the glass-wool plug, fit the tap-funnel (*Figure 1*).

There is little difficulty, by this procedure, in obtaining a level top to the column: the top must be kept covered with solvent, and undisturbed (hence the glass-wool plug: cotton-wool tends to adsorb dinitrophenylhydrazones). If the top of the column is uneven, irregular bands will result and the irregularities will become progressively greater as the bands are washed down the column.

At once run in from the tap-funnel a chloroform solution (50 c.c.) of a 1/1 mixture of benzaldehyde and *cyclo*hexanone 2 : 4-dinitrophenylhydrazones (200 mg). When the solution level has fallen to the glass-wool plug, add chloroform from the tap-funnel. As the chromatogram develops, an upper orange and a lower yellow band appear and unchanged reagent remains firmly adsorbed at the top of the column. Continue the elution with chloroform until the material of the yellow band has passed into the eluate. Change the receiver and elute the orange band on the column with 1/50 ethanol–chloroform. Evaporate eluates separately (see Figure 52) and determine yields and melting points of the two main fractions and of the mixed fraction, if any (*cyclo*hexanone derivative, m.pt 162°; benzaldehyde derivative, m.pt 237°; 80–100 mg of each). Recrystallize the fractions if necessary.

Clean and dry the column and reject the adsorbent.

Separation of 2 : 4-dinitrophenylhydrazones of many aldehydes and ketones can be effected on alumina [neutral or acid-washed: Brockmann Activity II–IV (see references)].

2 : 4-Dinitrophenylhydrazine and its salts can readily be removed from a crude 2 : 4-dinitrophenylhydrazone in benzene or benzene–chloroform on anhydrous magnesium sulphate, prepared as follows. Ordinary 'dried' magnesium sulphate is stirred with a 360° thermometer and heated on a clean tray until the temperature reaches 240°: the magnesium sulphate is then cooled in a vacuum desiccator and sieved (60–80 mesh).

(iii) SEPARATION OF LEAF PIGMENTS ON A COLUMN OF SEVERAL ADSORBENTS

Tswett's classical separations (*Ber. dtsch. bot. Ges.*, 1906, **24**, 384) were on calcium carbonate columns. Better results are obtained when three different adsorbents are used in the column (see *Figure 2*). The developed chromatogram is extruded for working up.

Complete the whole experiment within 24 hours.

Dry three or four clean, fresh green leaves (e.g. spinach leaves) or a handful of grass at 30–40° for 1 hour or overnight at room temperature. Chop the green-stuff fine and soak it for 1 hour in a mixture of light petroleum (b.pt 60–80°) (90 c.c.), benzene (10 c.c.) and methanol (30 c.c.). Filter the extract. Wash the filtrate carefully with water (4 × 50 c.c.) to remove the methanol (too vigorous shaking causes emulsions to form—centrifugation might then be necessary) and finally dry the solution over *sodium sulphate* (*not* magnesium sulphate). Concentrate the solution rapidly under reduced pressure to 5–10 c.c. by swirling the solution in a round-bottom flask, connected to the filter-pump and warmed on the steam (see *Figure 52*)—do not use an air leak or boiling-stick.

Wire on to the lower end of the *clean* column a piece of clean copper gauze (1·5 in. square) (see *Figure 2*). Push a small cotton-wool plug to the bottom of the column and then pack in the adsorbents either dry or, better, as slurries.

Dry-packing (see pp 3–4)

(*a*) 4 cm depth of alumina ('type H', Peter Spence and Sons Ltd, Widnes), (*b*) 6 cm of calcium carbonate (Hopkin and Williams Ltd, London) (previously dried at 80–100° for 30 minutes and then sieved, 80–100 mesh), (c) 6 cm of powdered sucrose (Hopkin and Williams, specially purified) (sieved, 80–100 mesh). Clean the sieves properly. Wet the column with light petroleum b.pt 60–80°) before running on the extract of pigments.

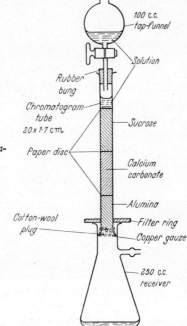

Figure 2. Adsorption chromatography apparatus with open-ended column for extrusion of the adsorbent

Wet-packing of adsorbents (pretreated as just described)

Slurry the alumina (8·0 g), calcium carbonate (5·3 g) and sucrose (7·0 g) separately in 50-c.c. conical flasks with light petroleum (b.pt 60–80°) (15, 30 and 20 c.c., respectively). Pour the alumina slurry into the column first. Tap the tube well (see p 5), rinse down the inside carefully with a little light petroleum, and, when the alumina has settled, drop on top a disc of filter-paper (15 mm diameter, cut with cork-borer No. 10). The liquid (*ca.* 5 cm depth) above the adsorbent breaks the fall of the disc, and the disc settles correctly without trapping air. When the solvent level has fallen to within 2 cm of the top of the alumina, pour the calcium carbonate slurry into the column. The calcium carbonate settles more slowly.

Tap the column, if necessary for 5 minutes. Rinse down the inside of the column with light petroleum, drop in a paper disc, and, when the solvent level has fallen sufficiently, add the sucrose slurry. Allow the sucrose to settle similarly, add a paper disc and then fit the tap-funnel (see *Figure 2*).

Run the concentrated extract of pigments on to the column and develop the chromatogram with 4/1 light petroleum (b.pt 60–80°)–benzene. Do not let the top of the column run dry. If the rate of percolation is unduly slow, apply air pressure, rather than suction, to the column: connect the top of the tap-funnel by pressure tubing to a compressed air supply via a T-piece, and insert the open limb of the T-piece in a cylinder of mercury, to give the required pressure head.

Bands appear on the column:

- (*a*)   Top. Olive-green (on sucrose): Chlorophyll-b
- (*b*)   Blue-green (on sucrose or on calcium carbonate): Chlorophyll-a
- (*c*)   Yellow (on calcium carbonate): Xanthophylls
- (*d*)   Bottom. Pink-orange (on alumina): Carotene(s).

When the chromatogram is fully developed, connect a filter-pump to the receiver and drain the column nearly dry. Take off the copper gauze. Carefully push the column of adsorbents out of the tube on to a sheet of paper with the aid of a glass rod flattened at one end. Alternatively, scoop out the coloured zones with a spatula. From each of the *coloured* zones elute the pigment with ether (10 c.c.) containing methanol (0·2 c.c.). Examine the filtered eluates in the visual spectrophotometer (see Chapter 28).

Note the positions of the principal absorption maxima and any end absorption for the various fractions.

Clean and dry the column and the spectrometer cells.

2
PARTITION CHROMATOGRAPHY

INTRODUCTION

MIXTURES are separable by partition chromatography if the components have different partition coefficients with respect to two liquid phases. One of the liquids is held absorbed in a solid (e.g. water in silica gel) with which the column is packed. The other liquid, in which the mixture is dissolved, is run on to the column, followed by this solvent liquid alone. The solutes are subjected to an infinite number of partitions as they pass down the column, and so they are separated, and eventually washed one by one into the eluate. The solid which supports the stationary liquid phase invariably has some adsorptive affinity for the solutes: but generally the solid is selected so that this is minimal.

REFERENCES

CASSIDY, *Technique of Organic Chemistry*, Interscience Publishers, Inc., New York, 1951, Vol. V.

LEDERER and LEDERER, *Chromatography*, Elsevier Publishing Company, Amsterdam, 1953.

MARTIN and SYNGE, *Biochem. J.*, 1941, **35**, 1358.

WILLIAMS, *An Introduction to Chromatography*, Blackie and Son Ltd, London, 1948; *The Elements of Chromatography*, Blackie and Son Ltd, London, 1954, Chapter 3.

SEPARATION OF Δ^1-TETRAHYDRO- AND cis-HEXAHYDRO-PHTHALIMIDES ON SILICA GEL

Stir the silica gel (British Drug Houses, chromatographic grade) (60 g) with water (27 c.c.; 45 per cent of the weight of the silica). If the silica is then slightly sticky, spread it out on paper to dry at room temperature.

Do not grease the tap of the chromatogram tube (*Figure 3*).

Shake benzene (500 c.c.) with water (100 c.c.) for 5 minutes. Half fill the chromatogram tube (tap closed) with the benzene, and push a plug of cotton-wool to the bottom of the tube and press down the wool firmly with a long glass rod (6 mm diameter). Add 4–5 g of the silica gel and press it down hard with the long glass rod for 2–3 minutes.   Add further portions (4–5 g each) of the silica gel and consolidate each in the column similarly.   It takes *ca.* 45 minutes to build up the column to a length of 40 cm with all of the silica gel.   (This packing procedure is essential.)   Level the top of the

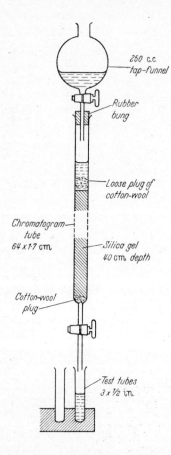

250 c.c.
tap-funnel

Rubber
bung

Loose plug of
cotton-wool

Chromatogram
tube
64 x 1·7 cm

Silica gel
40 cm depth

Cotton-wool
plug

Test tubes
3 x ½ in.

Figure 3.   *Apparatus for partition chromatography*

silica gel column, add a protecting plug of cotton-wool (*Figure* 3) and fit the tap-funnel. Wash the column with wet benzene (50 c.c.).

It is essential to keep the top of the silica gel column covered with solvent.

Run on to the column the mixture of imides (100 mg of each) (FICKEN, FRANCE and LINSTEAD, *J. chem. Soc.*, **1954**, 3730; FICKEN and LINSTEAD, *ibid*, **1952**, 4846) dissolved in the wet benzene (15 c.c.) *at* $\gg$ 1 *c.c./minute* and follow this with wet benzene at the same rate. Reject the first 20 c.c. of eluate.

Meanwhile prepare to test the eluate for imide (*cf.* RYDON and SMITH, *Nature, Lond.*, 1952, **169**, 922; REINDEL and HOPPE, *Chem. Ber.*, 1954, **87**, 1103). Put 12 test-tubes (5 × $\frac{5}{8}$ in.), each containing 1 c.c. of *ca.* 0·05N-potassium permanganate, in a rack. These are for generating chlorine. Into separate 9-cm Petri dishes put (*a*) 1/1 ethanol–acetone (10 c.c.) and (*b*) a mixture of saturated *o*-tolidine (4 : 4′-diamino-3 : 3′-dimethyldiphenyl) in 2N-acetic acid (5 c.c.) and *ca.* 0·05N-potassium iodide (5 c.c.)—use this mixture within 10 hours. Replace the covers on the dishes.

Collect 7-c.c. fractions of eluate from the column in test-tubes (3 × $\frac{1}{2}$ in.) mounted in wooden blocks (or use an automatic fraction collector). Test every other fraction for imide:

Crease a strip of filter-paper (Whatman No. 1; 15 × 1 cm) *ca.* 5 cm from one end *without fingering the longer end*. Put on to the paper, at the midpoint of the longer part, a drop of the solution and dry the paper with warm air from the blower ('Bylock' industrial air blower). Dip the paper momentarily in the ethanol–acetone and then blot, but do not dry, the strip with a folded filter-paper (15 cm). Add 10 per cent hydrochloric acid (1 c.c.) to one of the portions of permanganate and hang the longer part of the

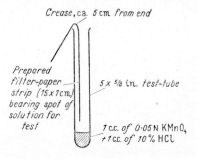

Figure 4. Treatment of test paper with dilute chlorine, in the detection of imides

Crease, ca. 5 cm from end

Prepared filter-paper strip (15 × 1 cm) bearing spot of solution for test

5 × 5/8 in. test-tube

1 c.c. of 0·05 N KMnO₄ + 1 c.c. of 10% HCl

paper strip in the chlorine in the test-tube (see *Figure 4*) for *4–5 minutes*. Then dip the paper strip in the *o*-tolidine–potassium iodide solution. The rapid appearance of a dark blue spot (at the correct position) indicates the presence of imide.

Mark the first tube which contains imide, and collect a further 30 fractions. Then test every other fraction for imide and stop collecting fractions when the test is negative.

Evaporate *every other* imide-containing fraction to dryness: run the fractions, rinsing the tubes with acetone, into small basins (flat-bottom, 4 cm diameter) placed in a large, *shielded* vacuum desiccator (12 in.), and evacuate this with the water pump. Take the melting points of the solids (Δ^1-tetrahydrophthalimide, m.pt 172°; *cis*-hexahydrophthalimide, m.pt 137°). Combine the solid and solution fractions appropriately, transferring the material with acetone to larger basins (flat-bottom, 8 cm diameter). Place these over concentrated sulphuric acid in the shielded desiccator, remove the solvent under reduced pressure, and record the weight of each imide and of the mixed fraction (if any) (tetrahydro-imide, 70–90 mg; hexahydro-imide, 50–80 mg).

Attach the bottom of the column to the filter-pump so that air is sucked through the column until the silica gel is quite dry. Then tip out the silica gel and reject it, and rinse and dry the column.

3

PAPER CHROMATOGRAPHY

INTRODUCTION

PAPER chromatography is generally a form of partition chromatography in which the stationary phase is the sorbed water always
present in filter-paper, the support the paper itself, and the moving
phase a solvent previously saturated with water. The method is
not invariably a partition process. Adsorption phenomena may be
involved so that the process may vary in different cases from purely
adsorption to purely partition chromatography.

A drop of a solution of the mixture is dried on the paper (sheet,
strip or disc) which is then mounted in a closed container so that it
can be irrigated with an organic liquid (downwards by gravity, or
upwards or horizontally by capillarity), without losses by evaporation.

The method is used for the qualitative analysis of organic mixtures
of all kinds, and it can be made quantitative by applying micro-
analytical methods, usually colorimetric, to the separated spots.
Its classical application is to the qualitative analysis of mixtures of
amino-acids.

REFERENCES

BALSTON and TALBOT, *A Guide to Filter Paper and Cellulose Powder
Chromatography*, Reeve Angel and Co. Ltd, London, and
Balston Ltd, Maidstone, 1952.
CASSIDY, *Technique of Organic Chemistry*, Interscience Publishers, Inc.,
New York, 1951, Vol. V.
LEDERER and LEDERER, *Chromatography*, Elsevier Publishing Com-
pany, Amsterdam, 1953.

(i) DESCENDING TWO-DIMENSIONAL PAPER CHROMATOGRAPHY.
SEPARATION AND IDENTIFICATION OF AMINO-ACIDS

A drop of a solution of the amino-acids is dried on a paper sheet near one corner.
Irrigation with the first solvent separates the original 'spot' into a single row of
'spots' (corresponding to constituents of the mixture). The first solvent is dried
off, the paper turned through a right angle, and the development continued in
the new direction with a second solvent. The two-dimensional development
results normally in complete resolution of the mixture (see *Figure 7*). After: he

13

paper has been dried once more, the separated amino-acid 'spots' are made visible by spraying with ninhydrin, and heating.

Run three papers simultaneously:

(a) *Reference amino-acids*

Use 0·01м-solutions in 10 per cent *iso*propanol ('Amino-acid standard solutions for chromatography', Shandon Scientific Company, London).

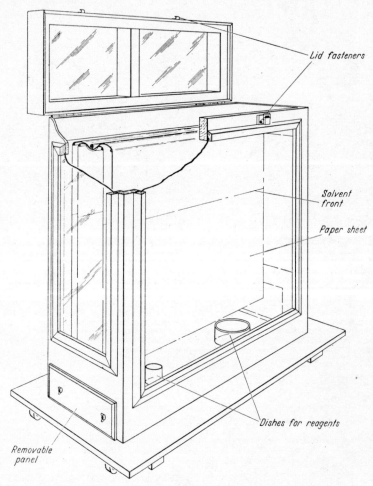

Figure 5. Paper chromatography cabinet (large, Shandon 'Two-Way')

14

Figure 6. Top of paper chromatography cabinet, with lid removed, showing three paper sheets in position: (a) *solvent front;* (b) *glass supporting rods;* (c) *heavy glass rod;* (d) *trough for solvent*

(b) *Urine*

Use your own urine, preferably collected immediately after rising (such urine has the highest amino-acid content).

(c) *A protein hydrolysate*

Hydrolyse serum albumin (Chapter 7) or gelatin: Reflux the protein (100 mg) overnight with concentrated hydrochloric acid (3 c.c.) and water (2 c.c.). Dilute the solution with water (*ca.* 10 c.c.), add 2N-sodium hydroxide solution to pH 7·0 [Use the B.D.H. Capillator (British Drug Houses Ltd, Poole) or use a 1/1 mixture of phenol red and bromocresol green indicator solutions (B.D.H.) externally— the colour changes are: pH 6·6, yellow; 6·8, greenish; 7·0, grey; 7·2, purplish; 7·4, deep purple], and make up the volume to 50 c.c. with water.

To avoid extraneous 'spots', handle the papers as little as possible and do not lay them on the bench.

Make a pencil mark on a sheet of filter-paper (Whatman No. 1, 24 × 24 in.; smaller papers are unsatisfactory) near one corner, 12 cm from each of the two edges. Fold one of these edges (about 9 cm down) over a glass supporting rod (from the cabinet) and fix a paper-clip, protected with folded filter-paper, over each end. Hang the paper up by mounting the glass rod on retort stands (*cf. Figure 12*). Apply the solution of amino-acids at the mark with a fine dropper, and allow the solution to soak into the paper until a spot 2 cm in diameter is formed. Dry the spot with warm air from the blower, and transfer the paper sheet, hanging from its rod, to the cabinet (Shandon large 'Two-Way' chromatography cabinet, see *Figure 5*). The wooden cabinets become contaminated with solvent. Use separate cabinets for the phenol and the butanol–acetic acid chromatograms.

Place the edge of the shorter end of each paper in the glass solvent-trough (see *Figure 6*) and place on top of the paper the heavy glass rod, which fits between pegs at one side of the cabinet. Remove the paper-clips.

The supporting rods must be slightly higher than the edge of the trough and must be ≮ 6 mm in diameter so that they do not sag below it in the middle ; otherwise the solvent will siphon over the surface of the paper sheet instead of flowing through the paper.

The supporting rods keep the papers hanging separate from one another (see *Figure 6*) and up to six sheets can be irrigated simultaneously three on each side of the trough.

15

Develop the papers first with aqueous phenol (the quantities are for running three papers)*. Add water (40 c.c.) to pure phenol (150 g) in a 1-litre beaker, and warm and stir the mixture on the steam-bath until the phenol dissolves. Cool the liquid (*ca.* 175 c.c.) to room temperature, and shake it gently with water (120 c.c.) for 5 minutes. If the emulsion does not separate in 5–10 minutes, run it through a large filter-paper into a second tap-funnel; two layers then form quite rapidly. Run the lower (phenol) layer into the trough, and place the upper layer†, with a few crystals of sodium cyanide, in a glass dish at the bottom of the cabinet, together with a second dish containing concentrated aqueous ammonia (1 c.c.). Replace the removable bottom panels and the fixing screws, and close the lid of the cabinet.

Start the development of the papers at mid-day and allow it to continue overnight. In cold weather, to prevent the phenol crystallizing, put the cabinet in a warm room or use a thermostatically controlled cabinet (25°).

Fasten each paper to its supporting rod by metal clips protected with folded filter-papers, and cut away the short length of paper in the trough with a razor blade. Lift each sheet out of the cabinet with its rod. Hang the sheets in the fume-chamber until the phenol has dried off *completely* (*ca.* 24 hours) or dry them with warm air from the blower (*ca.* 45 minutes for 3 papers). Mark the position of the 'phenol front' with pencil. Do not touch the paper with the fingers.

Then develop the papers with butanol–acetic acid. Shake butanol (210 c.c.) with acetic acid (90 c.c.) and water (33 c.c.), and keep the mixture at room temperature for 48 hours to allow time for the formation of the equilibrium quantity of butyl acetate.

Place the dried papers in a second cabinet reserved for butanol–acetic acid chromatograms, this time with the 'row of spots' parallel to the trough and nearest to it, i.e. with the phenol front perpendicular to the trough and with the marked origin spot uppermost. Place 30 c.c. of the butanol–acetic acid in a glass dish at the bottom of the cabinet and run the remainder into the trough. As the solvent moves fast, start the development late in the afternoon and stop it

---

* Make up the butanol–acetic acid for the second development at the same time.

† The two layers, being in phase equilibrium, produce vapours of the same composition. It is merely an economy to use the upper layer for saturating the air in the cabinet with solvent vapour.

first thing next morning. Remove the papers, mark the solvent front with pencil, and then dry the papers in the fume-chamber or with warm air from the blower, as before. With an efficient spray-gun [see *Figure 9* (b)] (e.g. Shandon) spray each paper *lightly*

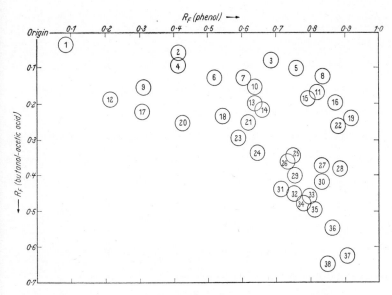

Figure 7. Amino-acids : two-dimensional paper chromatogram (phenol/butanol–acetic acid system)

1 *Cysteic acid.* 2 *Taurine.* 3 *Histidine.* 4 *Asparagine.* 5 *Tryptophane.* 6 *Threonine.* 7 *Citrulline.* 8 *Lysine.* 9 *Serine.* 10 *Sarcosine.* 11 *Arginine.* 12 *Aspartic acid.* 13 *3 : 5-Di-iodotyrosine.* 14 *Hydroxyproline.* 15 *Methionine sulphoxide.* 16 *1-Methylhistidine.* 17 *Glutamic acid.* 18 *Glutamine.* 19 *Histamine.* 20 *Glycine.* 21 *α-Alanine.* 22 *Proline.* 23 *Tyrosine.* 24 *β-Alanine.* 25 *Ornithine.* 26 *β-Aminoisobutyric acid.* 27 *β-Phenylalanine.* 28 *Ethanolamine.* 29 *α-Amino-n-butyric acid.* 30 *Methionine.* 31 *Methionine sulphone.* 32 *α-Aminoisobutyric acid.* 33 *Norvaline.* 34 *Valine.* 35 *γ-Amino-n-butyric acid.* 36 *isoLeucine.* 37 *α-Amino-noctanoic acid.* 38 *Leucine.*

on one side with a solution of ninhydrin in *n*-butanol (40 mg/40 c.c.; this is enough for *ca.* 10 sheets). Dry the papers either overnight in the fume-chamber or with *hot* air from the blower. Avoid scorching the paper. Mark the positions of the coloured spots with pencil to give a permanent record.

Identify as many of the amino-acids as possible with the help of the 'map' (*Figure 7*) and the sheet on which the reference amino-acids were run. Calculate the R_F values (see *Figure 8*). DENT (*Biochem. J.*, 1948, **43**, 169) gives a 'map' for the phenol–collidine system and other information.

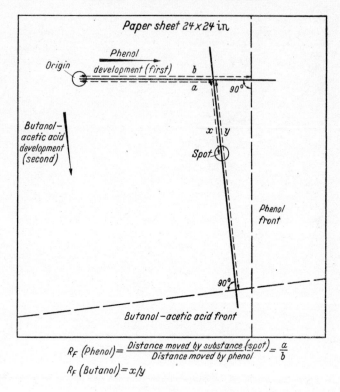

$$R_F \ (Phenol) = \frac{Distance\ moved\ by\ substance\ (spot)}{Distance\ moved\ by\ phenol} = \frac{a}{b}$$

$$R_F \ (Butanol) = x/y$$

Figure 8. Method of deriving R_F values from a two-dimensional paper chromatogram

(ii) Ascending One-dimensional Paper Chromatography. Separation of Dicarboxylic Acids

(*cf.* Cheftel, Munier and Macheboeuf, *Bull. Soc. Chim. biol., Paris,* 1952, **34**, 380.)

The apparatus consists of a tall glass cylinder (24 × 2·5 in.) fitted with a rubber bung which carries a glass support for strips of filter-paper [see *Figure 9* (a)].

Dilute 3·0 c.c. of concentrated aqueous ammonia to 5·0 c.c. with distilled water and add the solution to a mixture of ethanol (80 c.c.) and water (15 c.c.). Pour the solution into the glass cylinder. Fix one end of the paper strip (Whatman No. 1; 24 × 2 in. wide) to the glass support with paper-clips so that when the bung is later placed in position on the cylinder, the bottom end of the strip will dip into the solvent. Clamp the bung on to a retort stand and make a pencil mark on the paper about 3–4 cm above the future liquid level. Put the solution of dicarboxylic acids (0·2 g each of oxalic, malonic and adipic acids in 100 c.c. of water) on to the paper at the mark, with a fine dropper, making a spot about 1 cm in diameter. Dry the spot with hot air from the blower. Mount the paper in the cylinder and allow development of the chromatogram to proceed overnight.

Temperature fluctuations cause uneven running of the chromatogram. To protect the cylinder from draughts place it in a dust-bin or similar container (which must be large in comparison with the cylinder).

Next day, hang the paper strip in the fume-chamber to dry, or dry the strip with *cold* air from the blower. Spray* the dry strip

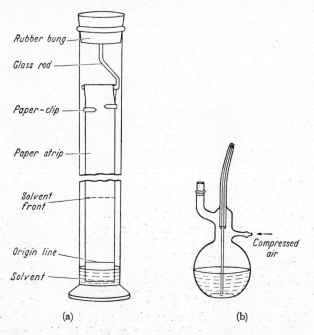

Rubber bung

Glass rod

Paper-clip

Paper strip

Solvent front

Origin line

Solvent

Compressed air

(a)   (b)

Figure 9. Apparatus for ascending one-dimensional paper chromatography: (a) *tall glass cylinder supporting filter-paper strips*, (b) *all-glass spray gun*

* It is important that the spray-gun [*Figure 9* (b)] should give a really fine spray.

19

lightly with ethanolic bromocresol green (100 mg/100 c.c., filtered) and *immediately afterwards* with 3 per cent aqueous lead acetate ('AnalaR'). Then allow the strip to dry, or dry it with warm air from the blower. The positions of the acids are indicated by yellowish spots (on a blue background). Record the R_F values for the adipic acid (fastest spot) and the malonic acid: that for oxalic acid is zero.

(iii) PAPER DISC CHROMATOGRAPHY.
A RAPID SEPARATION OF α-AMINO-ACIDS

(*cf*. GIRI and RAO, *Nature, Lond.*, 1952, **169**, 923; *J. Indian Inst. Sci.*, 1952, **34**, 95; PROOM and WOIWOOD, *J. gen. Microbiol.*, 1951, **5**, 681.)

A filter-paper disc, fitted with a central wick, is supported on a Petri dish which contains the irrigating solvent. The whole is enclosed between two larger Petri dishes (*Figure 10*, Shandon apparatus).

Shake *n*-butanol (20 c.c.) with acetic acid (5 c.c.) and water (25 c.c.) in a 100-c.c. separating funnel. Run the upper layer into the smallest Petri dish, placed inside the 13·5-cm diameter dish.

Use the largest Petri dish as a stand, and place on it with forceps a disc of filter-paper (Whatman No. 4, 12·5 cm). Put the transparent template (Shandon)—lifted with a rubber sucker—on top of the filter-paper, and, with a pencil, mark the positions of all 10 holes (the central hole, the 8 radial holes and the outer locating hole). Remove the template. Fold a filter-paper (Whatman No. 1, 15 cm) in half. Hold the marked paper disc down, at its edge, with a rubber sucker. With the other hand slide the folded paper over the marked disc nearly to its centre. Grip the papers near this point between finger and thumb, and pierce a central hole with the pointed tool. Make a wick by wrapping a 1·5–2·0-cm length of paper strip (Whatman No. 1, 2 cm wide) round the narrow shank of the tool. Push the wick three quarters of the way through the hole, still holding the filter-paper disc by means of the folded filter-paper. Then spot on, with a fine pipette, one drop of a solution containing cystine (as the ammonium salt), hydroxyproline and β-phenylalanine (0·01M with respect to each in 10 per cent *iso*propanol) at one of the marked positions and then at alternate marks, separate spots of each component (Shandon solutions, 0·01M in 10 per cent *iso*propanol). Dry the paper with warm air from the blower after application of each spot. Lay the paper

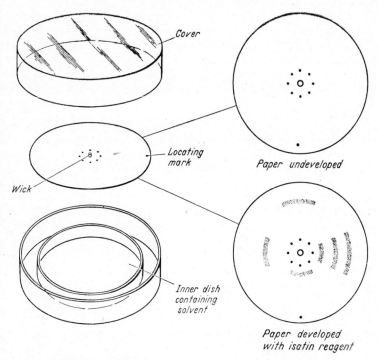

Figure 10. Shandon apparatus for paper disc chromatography

across the small Petri dish containing the irrigation solvent, the longer end of the wick downwards, and put on the cover (largest Petri dish). The solvent runs up the wick and spreads circularly on the filter-paper disc. When development is complete (20–25 minutes), lift the paper out with tweezers and dry it with warm air from the blower. Invert the largest Petri dish and pour into it 30 c.c. of a 0·2 per cent solution of isatin in 25/1 acetone–acetic acid (SAIFER and ORESKES, *Science*, 1954, **119**, 124). Hold the disc with the tweezers and immerse it in the acetone solution. Withdraw it at once. Dry the paper with *hot* air from the blower until the zones have developed (see *Figure 10*) (cystine, purplish; hydroxyproline, greenish; phenylalanine, bluish-grey). Mark the positions of the amino-acids to produce a permanent record.

Clean and dry the Petri dishes.

4

ION-EXCHANGE CHROMATOGRAPHY

INTRODUCTION

ION-EXCHANGE resins are organic macromolecular materials which carry acidic or basic functional groupings. Examples are sulphonated coal, polymethacrylic acid, and aminomethylated polystyrene. Such exchange resins are insoluble acids or bases, which form insoluble salts with ions from a solution. With their aid, double decomposition, salt splitting and neutralization reactions, deionization, and the recovery of ionic compounds from dilute solution can readily be effected.

In general, different ions possess different affinities for a given exchange material, so that separations may be effected, particularly easily if chromatographic methods are used.

REFERENCES

DUNCAN and LISTER, *Quart. Rev. chem. Soc., Lond.*, 1948, **2**, 307.
KUNIN and MYERS, *Ion Exchange Resins*, John Wiley and Sons, Inc., New York, 1950.
NACHOD, *Ion Exchange*, Academic Press Inc., New York, 1949.
REICHENBERG, *Research, Lond.*, 1953, **6**, 302.
STREATFIELD, *Chem. & Ind.*, **1953**, 1214.
WILLIAMS, *The Elements of Chromatography*, Blackie and Son Ltd, London, 1954, Chapter 4.

SEPARATION OF α-AMINO-ACIDS ON A CATION-EXCHANGE RESIN

(*cf.* PARTRIDGE and BRIMLEY, *Biochem. J.*, 1952, **51**, 628.)

The sulphonated polystyrene resin, $R(SO_3H)_x$ ('Zeo-Karb 225', The Permutit Co. Ltd, London) has been prepared by the emulsion polymerization method and consists of fine spherical particles (60–100 mesh). It therefore needs no grinding. The resin is only lightly crosslinked, having been made from styrene monomer containing *ca.* 4 per cent of divinylbenzene; exchange with organic ions of moderate size is thus facilitated. The exchange capacity of the resin is determined by titration with standard alkali, of a known weight of resin, slurried in water containing methyl red. The required amount of resin is wet-packed into chromatogram columns arranged as in *Figure 11*. The use of two or three columns of decreasing size aids the separation. Elution is by displacement development with dilute alkali.

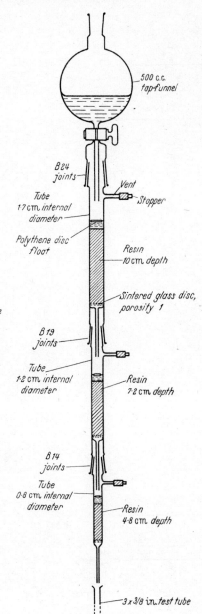

Figure 11. Apparatus for ion-exchange chromatography

It is helpful to incorporate an indicator into the resin. Stir the resin with a solution of phenolphthalein in aqueous ethanol and then wash the resin thoroughly with water on a filter, and dry the resin at 100°.

The columns have internal diameters of 1·7, 1·2, and 0·8 cm. Weigh out 9, 3·2, and 1·0-g lots of the dry resin, and slurry each separately with 2N-hydrochloric acid in 50-c.c. conical flasks. Fit the outlet of the smallest column with a rubber tube and screw clip, half-fill the column with distilled water, and then pour in the 1·0-g resin slurry through a small funnel, allowing the liquid to drain from the bottom of the column at the same time, but not allowing the resin to become uncovered. Then tighten the screw clip, and place a protecting polythene disc on the surface of the liquid in the column. Similarly fill the medium and large columns with the appropriate resin slurries, and finally fit the three columns together, the largest at the top (rubber-tubes with screw clips on the upper two column sections are, of course, discarded). Fit the tap-funnel into the top of the column assembly (see *Figure 11*), run in distilled water (100 c.c.), remove the rubber and clip from the bottom column, and allow the water to percolate through the system to wash the resin free from acid (test the eluate with wide-range indicator paper). Check that flow rate is 3–4 cm/min.

Dissolve aspartic acid, α-alanine and histidine hydrochloride (0·1 g of each) in water (50 c.c.). Retain 0·5 c.c. of this solution. Run the remainder of the solution on to the column and follow it with water (10 c.c.). Do not let the top column run dry: the small side vents allow the liquid levels in the column sections to be adjusted if necessary. Change the receiver and elute the column with *ca.* 0·075 N-sodium hydroxide solution. When the resin in the bottom column begins to change colour, adjust the rate of liquid flow to *ca.* 1 c.c./minute. Reject the eluate so far collected (*ca.* 610 c.c.). Continue to collect the eluate in 4-c.c. portions until there is an acid reaction to wide-range indicator paper, and then collect the eluate in 2-c.c. portions. It is convenient to use as receivers test-tubes (3 × ⅜ in.), mounted in wooden blocks (which hold 12). Number the tubes. When a tube becomes half-filled (2 c.c.), slide the block along so that the eluate is collected in the next tube, and so on. (An automatic fraction collector could be used.) Cease the collection of fractions (*ca.* 8 × 4 c.c. + 28 × 2 c.c.) when the eluate no longer gives a positive ninhydrin reaction. The test is performed as follows. Place single drops of the fractions on a 12·5-cm disc of filter-paper, dry the paper with hot air from the blower, spray the paper with ninhydrin solution (see Chapter 3), and dry it again. A purple spot indicates the presence of amino-acid.

Finally, analyse the fractions by paper chromatography. Lay the paper sheet (Whatman No. 1, 24 × 24 in.) on a glass plate and rule a pencil line parallel to, and 12 cm from, one edge of the paper.

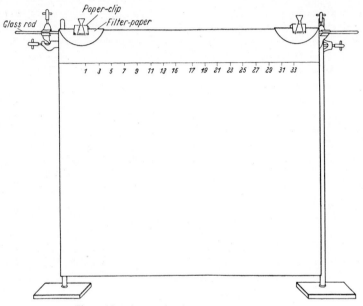

Figure 12. A paper sheet hung up on its supporting rod

Starting 6 cm from the left-hand end, write numbers (in pencil) '1', '3', '5', etc. at 3-cm intervals along the line. Hang the paper as shown in *Figure 12*. With a fine dropper, spot on in turn, two drops of each of the fractions 1, 3, 5, etc., at the marked points. Dry each spot on the paper with warm air from the blower before applying the next drop. Wash the dropper with distilled water between the applications of fractions. Finally spot on a drop of the original amino-acid solution and dry the spot with warm air from the blower.

Run the paper chromatogram with phenol, in the cabinet, over-night, as described in Chapter 3. Next day, remove the paper, dry it in the fume-chamber with warm air from the blower, and spray the paper with ninhydrin solution, and dry it with hot air.

From the paper chromatogram results, draw a diagram which indicates the distribution of the amino-acids in the fractions collected (*cf.* PARTRIDGE and BRIMLEY, *loc. cit.*).

Meanwhile wash the columns with *ca.* 0·075N-sulphuric acid until the eluate is acid, and then with distilled water until the eluate is neutral. Then tip the resin into the recovery bottle and rinse and dry the columns.

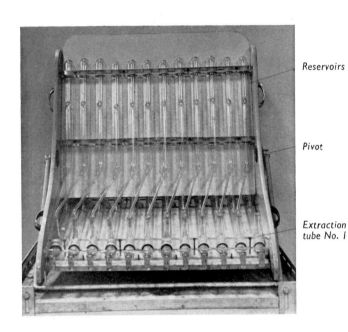

Reservoirs

Pivot

Extraction
tube No. 1

*Figure   13.   A twelve-tube multiple fractional extraction apparatus
(in resting position)*

5

MULTIPLE FRACTIONAL EXTRACTION
(LIQUID/LIQUID SYSTEM)

INTRODUCTION

THE technique of multiple fractional extraction, or countercurrent distribution, was developed by Craig and his colleagues for the separation of mixtures and for establishing the homogeneity and identity of organic substances. The method depends in principle on different solutes having different partitions with respect to the two phases of a liquid/liquid system.

The apparatus for the present experiment (*Figure 13*)* consists of a series of twelve extraction tubes (*Figure 14*). These are arranged so that after each equilibration the upper phase of each tube is transferred to the next tube via a reservoir, whilst the lower phase remains stationary: the first extraction tube is replenished with fresh upper phase after each transfer. The solutes, put into the first tube at the start of the experiment, progress through the series of extraction tubes at different rates, depending on their partition ratios between the two solvent phases.

REFERENCES

Theory: BUSH and DENSEN, *Analyt. Chem.*, 1948, **20**, 121.
Apparatus: CRAIG and POST, *ibid*, 1949, **21**, 500.
General: WEISSBERGER, *Technique of Organic Chemistry*, Interscience Publishers, Inc., New York, 1950, Vol. III, Chapter 4.

THEORY

Let the conditions of the experiment (partition coefficient and volumes of solvents) be such that, after each equilibration, a fraction p of a solute is found in the upper phase and a fraction $q = 1 - p$ in the lower.

Then, starting with unit quantity of solute, we arrive at the distribution shown in *Table I* (see pp 28-29).

---

* For the design, we are indebted to the National Institute for Medical Research, London.

27

Table I

Amount of Solute in Each Phase. (*Theoretical distribution of a solute at various stages in the operation of a 12-tube apparatus.*)

Tube No.	1		2		3		4		5		6	
Phase	U	L	U	L	U	L	U	L	U	L	U	L
Initial	—	1	—	—	—	—	—	—	—	—	—	—
Mix	p	q	—	—	—	—	—	—	—	—	—	—
First transfer	—	q	p	—	—	—	—	—	—	—	—	—
Mix	pq	q^2	p^2	pq	—	—	—	—	—	—	—	—
Second transfer	—	q^2	pq	pq	p^2	—	—	—	—	—	—	—
Mix	pq^2	q^3	$2p^2q$	$2pq^2$	p^3	p^2q	—	—	—	—	—	—
Third transfer	—	q^3	pq^2	$2pq^2$	$2p^2q$	p^2q	p^3	—	—	—	—	—
Eleventh transfer	—	q^{11}	$1\ pq^{10}$	$10\ pq^{10}$	$10\ p^2q^9$	$45\ p^2q^9$	$45\ p^3q^8$	$120\ p^3q^8$	$120\ p^4q^7$	$210\ p^4q^7$	$210\ p^5q^6$	$252\ p^5q^6$
Mix	$1\ pq^{11}$	$1\ q^{12}$	$11\ p^2q^{10}$	$11\ pq^{11}$	$55\ p^3q^9$	$55\ p^2q^{10}$	$165\ p^4q^8$	$165\ p^3q^9$	$330\ p^5q^7$	$330\ p^4q^8$	$462\ p^6q^6$	$462\ p^5q^7$

Table II

Weight of Solute in Each Phase (to nearest 0·1 mg). (*Theoretical distribution of gallic acid and* p-*hydroxybenzoic acid at the ultimate stage of operation of a 12-tube apparatus.*)

Tube No.	1		2		3		4		5		6	
Phase	U	L	U	L	U	L	U	L	U	L	U	L
Gallic acid	5·2	31·4	8·6	57·6	8·0	48·2	4·0	24·0	1·3	8·0	0·3	1·9
p-Hydroxybenzoic acid	0	0	0	0	0	0	0	0	0	0	0·5	0·1

Table I (continued)

Tube No.	7		8		9		10		11		12	
Phase	U	L	U	L	U	L	U	L	U	L	U	L
Initial	—	—	—	—	—	—	—	—	—	—	—	—
Mix	—	—	—	—	—	—	—	—	—	—	—	—
First transfer	—	—	—	—	—	—	—	—	—	—	—	—
Mix	—	—	—	—	—	—	—	—	—	—	—	—
Second transfer	—	—	—	—	—	—	—	—	—	—	—	—
Mix	—	—	—	—	—	—	—	—	—	—	—	—
Third transfer	—	—	—	—	—	—	—	—	—	—	—	—
Eleventh transfer	252 p^6q^5	210 p^6q^5	210 p^7q^4	120 p^7q^4	120 p^8q^3	45 p^8q^3	45 p^9q^2	10 p^9q^2	10 $p^{10}q$	1 $p^{10}q$	1 p^{11}	—
Mix	462 p^7q^5	462 p^6q^6	330 p^8q^4	330 p^7q^5	165 p^9q^3	165 p^8q^4	55 $p^{10}q^2$	55 p^9q^3	11 $p^{11}q$	11 $p^{10}q^2$	1 p^{12}	1 $p^{11}q$

Table II (continued)

Tube No.	7		8		9		10		11		12	
Phase	U	L	U	L	U	L	U	L	U	L	U	L
Gallic acid	0	0·3	0	0	0	0	0	0	0	0	0	0
p-Hydroxybenzoic acid	2·7	0·5	10·4	1·9	27·7	5·2	49·2	9·2	52·4	9·8	25·4	4·8

29

Thus at the second transfer, the solute is divided into the fractions q^2, $2pq$ and p^2 in tubes Nos. 1, 2 and 3 respectively: at the third transfer into fractions q^3, $3pq^2$, $3p^2q$ and p^3 in tubes Nos. 1, 2, 3 and 4 respectively, and so on. Hence, *at* the nth transfer in an apparatus with at least $(n + 1)$ tubes the fractions of the solute in the tubes will be given by the terms of the binomial expansion $(q + p)^n$. After the nth transfer there will be a mixing stage (equilibration of the phases), and then the fractions of solute in each tube will, of course, be distributed between the layers in the ratio p/q.

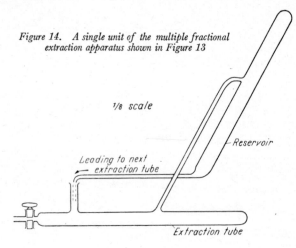

Figure 14.   A single unit of the multiple fractional extraction apparatus shown in Figure 13

1/8 scale

Reservoir

Leading to next extraction tube

Extraction tube

The distribution of the individual solutes of a mixture after n transfers in an apparatus can therefore be calculated, provided the distribution coefficients (K) of the solutes and the volumes of the two phases (U and L) in each tube are known.

In the experiment the solutes are gallic acid $(K = 0 \cdot 25)$ and p-hydroxybenzoic acid $(K = 8 \cdot 0)$, and the volume of the lower aqueous phase $L = 90$ c.c. in each tube (fixed by the design of the apparatus) and that of the upper ethereal phase $U = 60$ c.c.

By definition,

$$K = \frac{\text{mg/c.c. in } Upper \text{ phase}}{\text{mg/c.c. in } Lower \text{ phase}}$$

i.e.

$$K = (p/U)/\{(1 - p)/L\} = pL/(1 - p)U$$

$$\therefore p = KU/(KU + L)$$

30

Hence for gallic acid,

$$p = \frac{0 \cdot 25 \times 60}{0 \cdot 25 \times 60 + 90} = \frac{15}{105} = 0 \cdot 143,$$

and $\therefore$ $q = 0 \cdot 857$, and

for p-hydroxybenzoic acid,

$$p = \frac{8 \cdot 0 \times 60}{8 \cdot 0 \times 60 + 90} = \frac{480}{570} = 0 \cdot 842,$$

and $\therefore$ $q = 0 \cdot 158.$

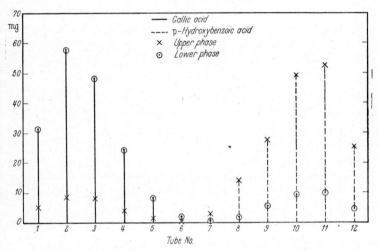

Figure 15. Theoretical distribution of gallic acid (200 mg) and p-hydroxybenzoic acid (200 mg) between ether (60 c.c) and water (90 c.c.) in a 12-tube apparatus

Substituting in the terms which represent the ultimate stage of operation of a 12-tube apparatus (*Table I*) for 200 mg of each of these solutes we obtain the distribution shown in *Table II*. The data of *Table II* are shown graphically in *Figure 15*. Thus at the end of the experiment pure gallic acid is present in tubes 1–5 and pure p-hydroxybenzoic acid in tubes 8–12.

EXPERIMENTAL PROCEDURE

Equilibrate the solvents; shake ether (1 litre) with distilled water (1·3 litre) in a separating funnel for 5 minutes. With the extraction

31

tubes in the horizontal position (*Figure 13*), introduce into each of the tubes 2–12 inclusive, 90 c.c. of the water layer. Add a further 100 c.c. of water layer to tube No. 2 and by moving the apparatus slowly backwards and forwards between the extreme positions, cause the excess of water to run through the series of tubes and eventually out at the end of the apparatus. All the lower halves of the tubes will then be exactly filled and all the glass surfaces wetted. Weigh out gallic and *p*-hydroxybenzoic acid (200 mg of each), dissolve them in 90 c.c. of the water layer and pour the solution into tube No. 1. Add 60 c.c. of the ether layer to tube No. 1 and rock the apparatus gently about 25 times to equilibrate the solutes between the two layers in the first tube. Allow the phases to separate, and turn the apparatus until the extraction tubes are in the extreme vertical position, so that the ether runs into the first reservoir. Then bring the apparatus back into its resting position (extraction tubes horizontal), so that the ether phase runs into the next tube No. 2. Add a fresh 60-c.c. portion of the ether to tube No. 1. Repeat the equilibration, and the transfer, and the addition to the first tube, until the upper phase reaches tube No. 12. Equilibrate and allow the phases to separate. Without delay, isolate the solute from each of the lower phases in tubes 1–6 and from each of the upper phases in tubes 7–12.

Evaporate each solution fraction under reduced pressure, in a 250-c.c. flask, on the steam-bath (see *Figure 52*): use the water pump for the ether and the mechanical pump with special trap (see *Figure 20*) for the aqueous fractions. Take each of the ethereal fractions to dryness and the aqueous fractions to 1–2 c.c. Then, each time, rinse down the inside of the flask with acetone (4 c.c.) from a pipette, transfer the solution with a dropping pipette to a tared flat-bottom dish (4 cm diameter), rinse the flask again with acetone (4 c.c.), and add the rinsings to the dish.

Place the 12 dishes over sulphuric acid in a large, shielded vacuum desiccator (12 in.) and evacuate it with the water pump. Find the weights of the solid residues, identify them by m.pt and mixed m.pt, and plot the distribution of the gallic acid and the hydroxybenzoic acid amongst the tubes of the extraction apparatus.

Empty the extraction apparatus, rinse it with distilled water and replace the cover.

6
IONOPHORESIS ON FILTER-PAPER

INTRODUCTION

THE different rates at which various organic ions move under the influence of an electric field, towards anode or cathode, enable separations to be effected of complex mixtures of organic materials, e.g. protein hydrolysates, blood serum, nucleic acids, and sugars. Rate of migration is not generally used as a criterion of purity.

The pH of the electrolyte is important. The behaviour of amino-acids illustrates this. In an acid buffer solution, an amino-acid will be present as the cation NH_3^+ ... CO_2H which will migrate towards the cathode (negative electrode), whilst in an alkaline buffer, the amino-acid, present as the anion NH_2 ... CO_2^-, will move towards the anode. At its isoelectric point the amino-acid is present as the true zwitterion NH_3^+ ... CO_2^- and will not migrate. Different amino-acids have different isoelectric points, so that at a given pH they will in general migrate at different rates in the electric field.

REFERENCES

Methods and apparatus:

CONSDEN and STANIER, *Nature, Lond.*, 1952, **170**, 1069.
DOUGLAS, *Rep. Progr. Chem.* [*Ann. Reports*], 1950, **47**, 80.
DURRUM, *J. Amer. chem. Soc.*, 1950, **72**, 2943; *J. Colloid Sci.*, 1951, **6**, 274.
FOSTER, *Chem. & Ind.*, **1952**, 1050.
WILSON, *Rep. Progr. Chem.* [*Ann. Reports*], 1951, **48**, 357.

Applications:

BULL, *Annu. Rev. Biochem.*, 1952, **21**, 185.
CANNAN and LEVY, *ibid*, 1950, **19**, 134.
CONSDEN and STANIER, *Nature, Lond.*, 1952, **169**, 783.
FOSTER, *loc. cit.*
GORDON, GROSS, O'CONNOR and PITT RIVERS, *Nature, Lond.*, 1952, **169**, 19.
LUNDGREN and WARD, *Annu. Rev. Biochem.*, 1949, **18**, 118.
WHISTLER and McGILVRAY, *ibid*, 1954, **23**, 79.

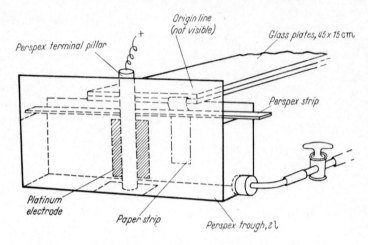

Figure 16. Diagram of apparatus for ionophoresis on filter-paper strips
(*showing anode end of the apparatus*)

SEPARATION OF AMINO-ACIDS

The apparatus (see *Figure 16*) consists of two Perspex troughs each containing a platinum electrode: the troughs are connected through a tap so that the liquid levels can be equalized. The filter-paper strips, the ends of which dip into the electrode troughs, are supported horizontally between two *clean* glass plates. There is provision for cooling. The current is provided by a power pack giving up to 1500 volts.

Fill both troughs with 5N-acetic acid until the liquid just covers the electrodes (about 4 litres are required), and open the tap in the connecting tube till the levels are the same; then close the tap.

Place a sheet of filter-paper (Whatman No. 31, extra thick, 27 × 20 in.) on a glass plate and rule a pencil line (the origin line) parallel to and four inches from the shorter edge of the paper. Cut three full-length strips, each about one inch wide, at right angles to the origin line. Handle the paper as little as possible.

If strips are cut from a 1-in. wide roll of the paper (Shandon Scientific Company), make certain that the origin lines are drawn on corresponding ends. This is to ensure that the papers will subsequently lie in the ionophoresis apparatus all in the same sense: the effects of directional variation in the texture of the paper are then obviated.

Use the following amino-acid solutions: (*a*) leucine (120 mg/100 c.c. of 10 per cent *iso*propanol); (*b*) glycine (120 mg/100 c.c. of 10 per cent *iso*propanol), and (*c*) a mixture of leucine, glycine and histidine hydrochloride (120 mg of each, in 100 c.c. of 10 per cent *iso*propanol).

Apply these solutions (about 0·2 c.c. of each), one to each strip at the origin line. Use a capillary dropper and dry each small drop on the paper with warm air from the blower before adding another drop. This procedure gives a small and concentrated spot of amino-acid(s). Spreading of the spot during the ionophoresis is then minimized.

Dip *each* end of *each* strip to 1 cm from the origin line in the liquid in the *anode* trough (red terminal) (in *this* experiment the cathode trough may become contaminated with amino-acids which have travelled too far). Lay each strip lengthwise on one of the glass plates of the apparatus with the origin line 2–4 cm in from the edge of the glass on the anode side (red terminal) : the ends of each strip dip into the troughs (*cf. Figure 16*), and the three origin lines should be level. Place the other glass plate on top of the papers and put the thin Perspex strips in place to hold the ends of the papers away from the electrodes. Place the covers over the troughs and electrodes.

Connect the electrodes to the terminals of the power pack (red to red and black to black) and switch on the current. Adjust the potential to about 1100 volts. If the current approaches 30 milliamperes, attach the cooling plate (a copper sheet with a zigzag cooling water tube brazed to one side) to the glass plates. Allow the current to pass for 3–3·5 hours. DURING THIS PERIOD, ON NO ACCOUNT TOUCH THE APPARATUS WITHOUT FIRST SWITCHING THE CURRENT OFF.

Switch off the current and disconnect the power pack. Remove the trough covers and slide off the upper glass plate. Slip a Perspex strip under the papers at the anode end and lift out the papers (wet filter-paper is easily torn). Then fasten the ends of the papers to the Perspex strip with metal clips so that the papers can be hung up. Dry them with warm air from the blower. Spray *both* sides of each paper lightly with a solution of ninhydrin (40 mg/40 c.c. of *n*-butanol) and dry the papers with hot air from the blower. Identify the spots and mark their positions with pencil to give a permanent record.

7

ISOLATION AND PURIFICATION
OF A PROTEIN

(CENTRIFUGATION, CRYSTALLIZATION
DIALYSIS AND LYOPHILIZATION)

INTRODUCTION

THIS exercise, which gives experience in the handling of delicate biological material, involves the separation and crystallization of albumin from horse blood :

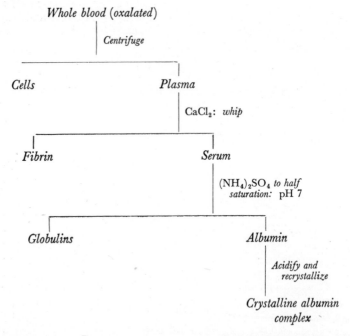

Finally, the crystalline ammonium sulphate–albumin complex is dissolved in water, and the solution dialysed. The albumin solution, free of salts, is freeze-dried to yield the solid protein.

Figure 17. Photomicrograph of horse serum albumin crystals (clusters of needles, sometimes described as 'palm leaves')

EXPERIMENTAL

REFERENCES

ADAIR and ROBINSON, *Biochem. J.*, 1930, **24**, 993.
HOPKINS, *J. Physiol.*, 1900, **25**, 306.

EXPERIMENTAL

Notes: (*1*) This experiment is lengthy but requires only intermittent attention.   The blood must be fresh.

(*2*) The centrifuge (e.g. the M.S.E. Medium Centrifuge, Measuring and Scientific Equipment Ltd, London) must not be mishandled since this could be dangerous.   Always load the rotor-head so that radial stresses are equalized.   Two, three, four or six tubes can therefore be centrifuged at one time.   Balance the tubes and their contents against one another to within 0·1 g.   Place a centrifuge tube, assembled in the metal cup as in *Figure 18*, on one balance-pan and put the mixture to be centrifuged into the glass tube.   Balance the other centrifuge tubes, assembled similarly, against the first, filling them either with the mixture or with water.

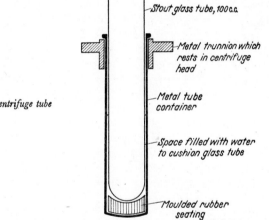

Figure 18.   Details of centrifuge tube

— Stout glass tube, 100 c.c.

— Metal trunnion which rests in centrifuge head

— Metal tube container

— Space filled with water to cushion glass tube

— Moulded rubber seating

Mount the tubes symmetrically on the head, and close the lid of the centrifuge.   Switch on the motor and accelerate it to 2500 r.p.m. during *ca.* 5 minutes.   At the end of the required period of centrifugation, reduce the speed very slowly to zero during at least 10 minutes.   If deceleration is rapid, the contents of each tube start swirling and the centrifugate and supernatant liquor mix.

Keep oxalated horse blood (50 c.c.) (obtained by direct bleeding at the slaughter house into 10 per cent aqueous potassium oxalate, 10 c.c./litre of blood) (or from Burroughs Wellcome & Co., London) overnight in the refrigerator (*ca.* + 2°). Next morning siphon off the top layer (the plasma), without disturbing the lower layer (red and white cells). Centrifuge the plasma (25 c.c.) for 20 minutes at 2500 r.p.m., decant it from any red cells, and then put it in the refrigerator for 1 hour. Stir calcium chloride (0·6 c.c.; 2 per cent of $CaCl_2$) into the plasma with a glass rod. Collect most of the precipitated fibrin on the stirring rod by gentle whipping, and filter off the remainder. Stir (mechanically) the filtrate (serum) (*ca.* 20 c.c.), treat it slowly with an equal volume of filtered saturated ammonium sulphate solution, and maintain the pH at 7 (wide-range indicator paper or B.D.H. 'Capillator') by the dropwise addition of 2N-sodium hydroxide. Keep the mixture at room temperature for 1 hour and remove the precipitated globulins by centrifugation at 2500 r.p.m. for 30 minutes.

Chill the supernatant solution in the refrigerator. Stir a 10-c.c. portion of the solution and titrate it with 10 per cent acetic acid to opalescence. Then stir the rest of the solution and treat it with the same proportion of acetic acid*. Mix the two portions well, treat the mixture with an additional 1 c.c. of 10 per cent acetic acid, and keep it overnight at + 2°.

The albumin crystallizes out in fine needle aggregates (see *Figure 17*). Examine it under the microscope. Remove the albumin by centrifugation (2500 r.p.m.; 30 minutes) and dissolve it in the minimum of water (*ca.* 50 c.c.). Filter the solution through a fluted paper, and then stir in filtered saturated ammonium sulphate solution until a cloudiness appears. Leave the solution to crystallize overnight at + 2°.

Examine the albumin once more under the microscope, and then dissolve the albumin in the minimum of water (20–30 c.c.). Dialyse this solution, in a loop of *thin* cellophane tubing (50 × 2 cm), against running water for *ca.* 6 hours and then overnight against distilled water (1 litre) at + 2° (apparatus, see *Figure 19*): first soak the tubing in water and then insert a funnel in one end to facilitate the filling.

Pour the dialysed (salt-free) albumin solution into a 250-c.c. round-bottom flask (with a B24 socket). Dip the flask into a dish containing solid carbon dioxide and alcohol, and rotate the

---

* In this experiment the whole of the solution could be titrated, but on a larger scale this would be tedious.

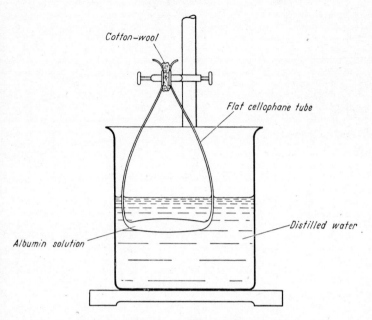

Figure 19. *Apparatus for dialysis of albumin solution*

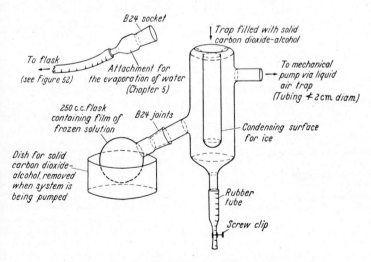

Figure 20. *Apparatus for freeze-drying (i.e. evaporation of ice)*

flask so that the albumin solution freezes as a thin layer over the inside. At once connect the flask to the special vacuum trap (see *Figure 20*) which is charged with solid carbon dioxide and alcohol, and switch on the pump. The ice in the frozen solution sublimes slowly into the trap and leaves the freeze-dried (or lyophilized) albumin as an almost colourless powder. This should readily dissolve in water to a clear solution. Weigh the albumin powder (yield, 30–40 mg) and transfer it to a labelled bottle. Thaw and drain the trap.

NOTE

USE OF SIMPLE MICROSCOPE

Place a clean slide on the microscope stage, near one edge. Put a trace of the substance on to the centre of the slide—transfer solids with a micro-spatula, and suspensions by means of a glass rod (a dropper would require very careful control). Turn the focusing screw so as to raise the objective. Move the slide to bring the substance directly under the objective. Then move the objective downwards to *ca.* 2 mm above the slide: *do not screw the objective into contact with the slide*. Look through the eyepiece, adjust the mirror for good illumination, and slowly raise the objective until the field is in focus. Complete the focusing with the fine adjustment.

Subsequently remove and clean the slide, and replace the microscope (clean) in its case.

8

FRACTIONAL DISTILLATION

(UNDER CONTROLLED REDUCED PRESSURE)

INTRODUCTION

GENERALLY, a boiling mixture of miscible liquids and the vapour with which it is in phase equilibrium possess different compositions, the vapour being richer in the more volatile component(s). Condensation of the vapour therefore gives a liquid enriched with the more volatile component(s) of the mixture. A further enrichment can be effected by repetition of the process, i.e. boiling of the enriched liquid and condensation of the vapour in phase equilibrium with it.

Fractional distillation consists of passing the vapours from the boiling mixture through a vertical column, usually containing a packing of high surface area, so that ascending vapour and refluxing liquid are brought into intimate contact throughout its length. As a result of heat exchange between vapour and liquid all along the column, a whole series of vaporizations and condensations is effected continuously. Under total reflux the column reaches a state of dynamic equilibrium and there is a composition gradient along it.

The efficiency of a fractionating column depends on:

(a) *Number of theoretical plates*—The theoretical degree of enrichment, given by the single vaporization and condensation, described above, can be calculated from Raoult's law.

Ideally, the partial pressure of a component in the vapour in equilibrium with a mixture of miscible liquids is proportional to the molar fraction of that component in the liquid.

A column which gives this degree of enrichment has an efficiency of 1 theoretical plate. The higher the plate value of a column, the smaller is the difference between the boiling points of compounds which can be separated. Column efficiency is also expressed in H.E.T.P. (height equivalent to a theoretical plate) = height of column/no. of theoretical plates. Plate values vary with the test mixture, which must therefore be specified, and may be

25–50 per cent greater when the column is under total reflux than when operating at a reflux ratio of *ca*. 10/1 (i.e. 10 parts of liquid returned to the column/1 part collected).

(b) *Hold-up*—This is the amount of material in the column during its operation. The hold-up should not exceed 10 per cent of the volume of any one component to be separated.

(c) *Pressure drop*—This is the difference in pressure between the still-pot and the column head. It depends on the column size, the packing and the rate of distillation (throughput), and imposes a lower limit on the pressure obtainable in the still-pot.

Thus if the pressure drop were 5 mm of mercury, then with head pressures of 20, 1, 0·1 and 0·001 mm, the pressure in the still-pot would be 25, 6, 5·1 and 5·001 mm.

A fractionating column must be so operated as to minimize disturbance of the dynamic equilibrium and thence composition gradient in the column. The following points must therefore be observed:

(*1*) The final enriched material or pure component at the top of the column must be removed *slowly*. The reflux ratio should be high; the optimum value is numerically equal to the plate no. of the column. Alternatively, the take-off can be intermittent: the take-off tap is opened momentarily every few minutes (which could be done automatically).

The column is then operated under total reflux conditions (of highest efficiency) for the greater part of the time.

(*2*) The heat input to the still-pot must be controlled to maintain constant throughput, irrespective of b.pt changes. For columns with metal gauze packing (e.g. Stedman type) there is an optimum throughput for maximum efficiency.

With less throughput, the packing is incompletely wetted: at higher throughputs the vapour velocity is too high for attainment of vapour/liquid equilibria.

The column must be flooded initially to wet the packing.

(*3*) Heat loss from the column must be prevented. Above *ca*. 60°, heat loss is appreciable; this decreases the amount of vapour which can reach the column head and causes flooding. A heating jacket must compensate exactly for the heat loss. If the column is superheated, the low-boiling constituents pass directly from the still-pot to the column head.

For a liquid boiling at 180°, a plate value of 90 will be reduced to about 20 if the column is superheated by 20°.

(*4*) The pressure must be kept constant. At low pressures, even very small variations at once cause either flooding or cessation of reflux. The pressure control mechanism therefore can hardly be other than elaborate.

REFERENCES

General:

CARNEY, *Laboratory Fractional Distillation*, The Macmillan Company, New York, 1949.

MORTON, *Laboratory Technique in Organic Chemistry*, McGraw-Hill Book Company, Inc., New York, 1938, Chapter 4.

WEISSBERGER, *Technique of Organic Chemistry*, Interscience Publishers, Inc., New York, 1951, Vol. IV.

Column packings:

Dixon gauze rings, DIXON, *J. Soc. Chem. Ind., Lond.*, 1949, **68**, 88, 119.

Fenske helices, FENSKE, LAWROSKI and TONGBERG, *Industr. Engng Chem.* (*Industr.*), 1938, **30**, 297.

Stainless steel helices, TODD, *Industr. Engng Chem.* (*Anal.*), 1945, **17**, 175.

Stedman conical packing, BRAGG, *ibid*, 1939, **11**, 283.

Pressure regulation:

COULSON and WARNE, *J. sci. Instrum.*, 1944, **21**, 122.

HERSHBERG and HUNTRESS, *Industr. Engng Chem.* (*Anal.*), 1933, **5**, 344.

SEPARATION OF LAURIC AND MYRISTIC ESTER

Description of the distillation apparatus (see *Figure 21*)

The column (*ca.* 25 plates with respect to benzene/carbon tetrachloride) is a 2 ft. length of 'Veridia' precision-bore tubing (Chance Bros, Smethwick, Nr Birmingham), packed with 20-mm diameter, Stedman type, cup-and-plate gauze elements. The packing must not be disturbed. The gauze elements were punched (at the Chemical Research Laboratory, Teddington) from 50-mesh *annealed* stainless steel gauze (Johnson, Matthey and Co. Ltd, London). The castor oil lubricant, used when these elements were inserted in the tube, was subsequently extracted with acetone.

The column heating jacket is wired in two sections, each run off a 'Variac' transformer (Zenith Electric Co. Ltd, London), and gives temperatures up to 280°. The heater for the air-bath which surrounds the 250-c.c. two-necked still-pot is controlled similarly and gives temperatures up to 300°.

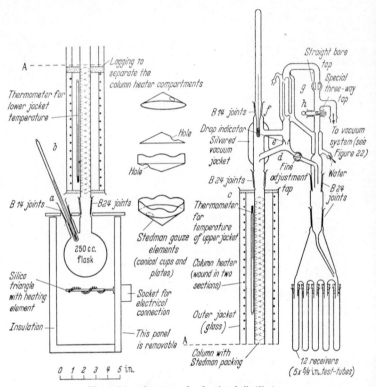

Figure 21. Apparatus for fractional distillation

The column head (*Figure 21*) is a total condensation, variable take-off type, with hollow-barrel taps. The take-off tap is grooved to facilitate fine adjustment of the reflux ratio.

The pressure at the column head is kept constant, at any required setting in the range 10 mm of mercury to atmospheric pressure, by a modified Coulson–Warne manostat system (see *Figure 22*). There are two 5-litre reservoirs, *m* and *o*, connected through an electromagnetically operated air-valve *n*. A mechanical pump ('Speedivac' ISP 30, High Vacuum, Edwards Ltd, Crawley), controlled (to operate intermittently) by a mercury manostat *r* through a relay, maintains in the reservoir *o* a roughly constant pressure (indicated on the manometer *l*) which has, of course, to be somewhat lower (say, 5 mm of mercury lower) than that required

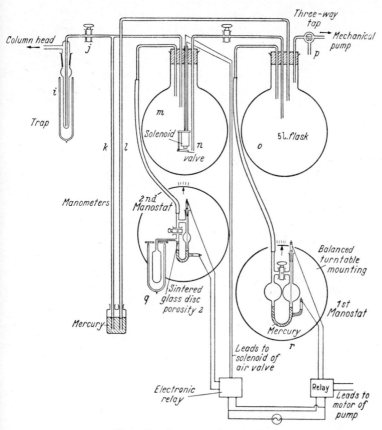

Figure 22. Pressure regulation system

at the column head. The pressure in the reservoir *m*—to which the column is connected—is kept constant at the required value (indicated on the manometer *k*) by the opening and closing of the valve *n*. Because the pressure difference across this valve is small (*ca.* 5 mm of mercury), it operates particularly readily. The large capacity of the reservoirs and the smallness of the pressure difference between them serve to eliminate entirely pressure fluctuations at the column head. The valve n is controlled through an electronic relay by a second manostat q, the bulb (100 c.c.) of which is kept at a constant temperature* so that the 'reference pressure' in it remains constant. There is then no drift of the pressure setting (at the column head) with changes in room temperature.

Changes in atmospheric pressure are without effect on the pressure maintained at the column head (because the control is effected by a fixed volume of air at constant temperature in the bulb of the manostat q). There is, of course, a change in the pressure reading on the manometer with change in atmospheric pressure, but the *difference* between these pressures (which is the pressure at the column head) remains constant.

Preliminaries

Mount the column vertically, flame the top and the bottom joint, spread a little 'Audco' sealing compound (lubricant No. 657, Audley Engineering Co. Ltd, Newport, Shropshire) on the ground-glass surfaces and connect the head and still-pot (see *Figure 21*). Grease the taps and the joints of the head and receiver with 'Apiezon M' (see p 80). Silicone grease is unsatisfactory for taps and *must not be used on the head joints*; if any silicone grease is washed down on to the gauze elements of the column these will cease to be wetted by the refluxing liquid and the column will lose its efficiency.

Run the mixture of esters (80 c.c., 1/1) into the still-pot, through the side neck at a, and insert a boiling-stick or an anti-bumping tube (p 68) to promote smooth ebullition. Grease the joint of the side-neck a with silicone grease (high-vacuum grade) and put the thermometer pocket in place. Put a few drops of medicinal paraffin in the pocket so that the thermometer makes thermal contact with it.

Lag the exposed parts of the column head with cotton-wool, and turn on the water to the condenser.

Switch on the heaters of the air-bath and column jacket so that these warm up whilst the apparatus is being evacuated.

Setting of the pressure regulation system (see Figures 21 and 22)

Make sure taps g and j are open. Close the taps h and p to the atmosphere and switch on the electricity supply to the pump

---

* The bulb is surrounded by a Dewar flask which effectively eliminates temperature fluctuations over short periods (e.g. 1 day). For longer periods the Dewar flask should be kept filled with a mixture of ice and water.

and relays. Rotate the manostat r clockwise so that contact is made between the mercury and the tungsten wire: the pump then starts. Rotate the manostat q anticlockwise to break contact between the mercury and the tungsten wire: the air-valve between the reservoirs then opens. The pressure drops more rapidly in the first reservoir (indicated on manometer l) than in the second (manometer k).

Read the barometer. When the pressure indicated on the first manometer is ca. 5 mm of mercury less than that required at the still head (15 mm Hg), close the tap on the manostat r (to enclose 'reference air', at ca. 10 mm Hg pressure in this case) and rotate the manostat anticlockwise until the mercury just breaks contact with the tungsten wire.

The manostat will then control the pump so that it keeps the pressure in the reservoir o at the set value (10 mm Hg). If the pressure in the reservoir starts to rise, there is a change in the levels of the mercury in the manostat, and the electrical circuit to the pump is made. The pump reduces the pressure again, the mercury levels change, and the circuit is soon broken and the pump stopped.

When the pressure at the column head (and in the reservoir m), indicated on the manometer k, has fallen to the required value (15 mm Hg), close the tap of the second manostat q and rotate this manostat clockwise until the mercury just makes contact with the tungsten wire.

The slightest tendency for the pressure at the column head to rise will result in the contact being broken, with consequent opening of the air-valve.

If it becomes necessary to alter the pressure at the column head, open the tap of the second manostat q and either admit air to the reservoir m via tap h or allow air to be extracted (by the pump and first reservoir) as required. When the desired new pressure is indicated on the manometer k, close the tap of the manostat q and rotate the manostat clockwise until the mercury just makes contact again with the tungsten wire.

Equilibration of the column

When the pressure regulating system has been set, immerse the trap i in a Dewar flask of liquid nitrogen. Adjust the voltage across the lower section of the column heater to give a temperature, shown on thermometer b, a few degrees lower than the temperature (indicated at a) of the vapour in the still-pot. Adjust the upper section of the column heater to give a temperature at c a few degrees lower than the expected b.pt of the first fraction (ca. 143° at 15 mm Hg). Increase the voltage across the still-pot heater (air-bath) to increase the rate of boiling so that the column floods along its entire length. Then reduce the air-bath temperature until flooding ceases and the rate of reflux at the drop indicator e is ca. 2 c.c.

(i.e. *ca.* 30–40 drops)/minute. Adjust the column heaters to maintain the correct temperatures at *b* and *c*. Run the column under total reflux for 1 hour to establish equilibrium.

Tabulate at intervals: time, still-pot vapour temperature (at *a*) and air-bath voltage, column jacket temperatures (at *b* and *c*) and voltages, column head temperature (i.e. b.pt, at *f*) and reflux rate (at *e*), and head pressure (i.e. barometric pressure minus reading on manometer *k*): subsequently add reflux ratio and fraction characteristics (see below). This log makes control of the distillation system easy.

The fractionation

After the equilibration of the column, turn the take-off tap *d* in the head to give a reflux ratio (p 42) of 15–20/1 and start collecting fractions. For as long as the b.pt remains constant, the reflux ratio can be reduced to 5/1. Change the receiver tube (*1*) when the b.pt changes, (*2*) when the refractive index of the distillate changes (watch for striations in the liquid in the receiver,

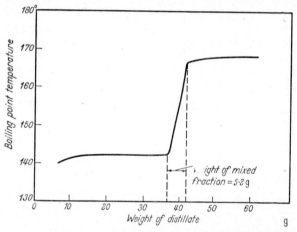

Figure 23. *Distillation curve for a mixture of methyl laurate and methyl myristate (at* 15 mm Hg)

as the drops fall in), and (*3*) when the volume of a fraction reaches 5 c.c. Record the b.pt of each fraction and the reflux ratio during its collection.

Keep writing the log. Adjust the still-pot and column heaters to keep the rate of reflux (at *e*) constant and to maintain the correct temperature differences between *a* and *b*, and *c* and *f*.

The column can be left at any time under total reflux, provided the liquid is stable. If the reflux is interrupted, flooding of the packing and equilibration of the column must be repeated before collection of distillate is resumed.

When *ca.* 50–60 c.c. of distillate have been collected, close down the apparatus thus. Switch off the heaters, open the taps on the manostats, switch off the power supply to the pump and relays, close taps *d* and *g* in the head, and open taps *h* and *p* to the atmosphere. Remove the Dewar flask of liquid nitrogen from the trap *i*.

Determine the weights of the fractions, and the melting points of the methyl myristate fractions (b.pt *ca.* 167° at 15 mm Hg). Plot a graph of b.pt against total weight distilled (see *Figure 23*) and mark in the weight of the mixed fraction.

Allow the column to cool under vacuum, then open tap *g*. Clean the column (and head) by refluxing a solvent (e.g. acetone) through for 15–30 minutes. Leave the apparatus, including the column joints, clean and dry.

9

VACUUM SUBLIMATION

AND A NOTE ON SMALL-SCALE MOLECULAR DISTILLATION OF SOLIDS

INTRODUCTION

MANY organic compounds have appreciable vapour pressures at temperatures below their melting points and can therefore be sublimed—the solid is converted by heat to vapour (without intermediate liquid stage) and the vapour condensed to solid on a cold receiver. Sublimation is usually carried out under reduced pressure in order to keep down the temperature.

Purification of a substance by sublimation is effective when the contaminants have a different order of volatility. The method can be particularly useful for the purification of compounds which solvate or deliquesce.

REFERENCES

MORTON, *Laboratory Technique in Organic Chemistry*, McGraw-Hill Book Company, Inc., New York, 1938, Chapter 11.

WEISSBERGER, *Technique of Organic Chemistry*, Interscience Publishers, Inc., New York, 1951, Vol. IV, Chapter 7.

(i) MICRO-SUBLIMATION

Determine the m.pt (p 54ff) of the solid substance. Place about 50 mg (or less) of the solid in the bottom of the outer tube of a 'cold-finger' apparatus (see *Figure 24*). Lightly smear the joints longitudinally with grease ('Apiezon M'), assemble the apparatus, connect it to the pumping system (read p 78), and cautiously evacuate the apparatus*. Run water through the cold-finger. Place the apparatus in an oil-bath as shown (*Figure 24*) and slowly raise the temperature until sublimation occurs at a convenient rate, or to about 30° below the m.pt of the solid, whichever temperature is the lower. Do not raise the temperature too rapidly or the substance may spatter. During the sublimation note the

---

* On a cold day, before attempting to turn the taps of the high vacuum system, warm them *slightly* with warm air from the blower, to soften the grease. Do not warm the grease too much or it will flow out from the tap seatings.

pressure (see p 79) inside the apparatus and the oil-bath temperature.

When sublimation ceases (some residue is normally left), remove the heating bath and allow the apparatus to cool. Then cautiously release the vacuum. Withdraw the cold-finger carefully and

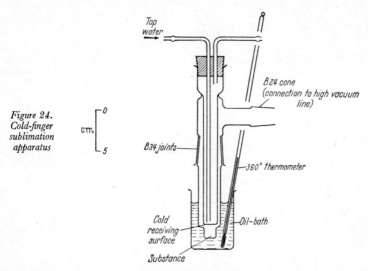

Figure 24.
Cold-finger
sublimation
apparatus

Top water →

B24 cone
(connection to high vacuum
line)

cm
0
5

B34 joints

—360° thermometer

Cold
receiving
surface

Oil-bath

Substance

detach the sublimate with a micro-spatula on to a clean watch glass. Take the m.pt of the sublimate, clean the apparatus, and repeatedly sublime the solid to constant m.pt. Finally, transfer the solid into two cleaned and dried specimen tubes, and stopper or seal them and label them. (The material needs no additional drying before an analysis, etc.)

Clean and dry the sublimation apparatus.

(ii) PREPARATIVE-SCALE SUBLIMATION

Determine the m.pt of the solid substance. Roll a 15-cm diameter filter-paper into a tube and insert this right down the neck of a clean high-vacuum retort (bulb 75 c.c.). Then pour a weighed quantity (*ca.* 5 g) of the powdered substance down the tube into the bulb of the retort. Tap the paper tube well and withdraw it. Smear the joints of the retort and receiver lightly with grease ('Apiezon M'), and connect them together and to the vacuum line (see *Figure 25*). Evacuate the apparatus cautiously, to avoid spattering of the solid, and by means of an electric furnace slowly raise the temperature of the retort until sublimation occurs. This is usually at 50–150° at 10^{-4}–10^{-5} mm. (Do not melt the solid.) Record the temperature and pressure at which sublimation occurs.

When sublimation ceases, allow the retort to cool, release the vacuum cautiously, and disconnect the retort and receiver. Wipe the joints free from grease with cotton-wool moistened (*not soaked*)

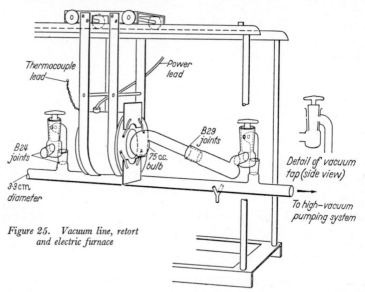

Figure 25. Vacuum line, retort and electric furnace

with benzene. Remove the sublimate from the neck of the retort with a long-handled spatula. Record the yield and m.pt of the product, and transfer it to a labelled bottle or tube.

Clean and dry the retort and receiver.

(iii) FRACTIONAL SUBLIMATION

In the manner described above, introduce the mixture of solids (e.g. phthalimide and phthalic anhydride) into the bulb of a retort: do not fill the bulb more than about one third full. Heat the retort, connected to the line (*Figure 25*), so that sublimation occurs slowly. Record the temperature and pressure.

At the end of the experiment, there will be zones of sublimate in the neck of the retort. Carefully remove the material of each zone in turn, with a long-handled spatula, and record the yields and melting points. If necessary, resublime the fractions separately. Finally transfer the solids to labelled specimen tubes.

A Note on Small-scale Molecular Distillation of Solids

If sublimation of an organic solid or mixture of solids fails to occur in a high vacuum even at temperatures approaching the melting point, it may be convenient, provided the material is stable, to raise the temperature above the melting point: the liquid will then be subjected to short-path or molecular distillation (see p 72). The liquid remains quiescent and the distillate collects slowly as a solid on the condensing surface of the apparatus.

10
FINAL PURIFICATION OF SOLIDS FOR ANALYSIS

INTRODUCTION

BEFORE an organic compound is submitted to elementary analysis and/or quantitative physical measurements it must be purified as completely as possible. Likely trace contaminants in a substantially pure solid are atmospheric dust, filter-paper fibres, particles of glass, and occluded solvent or moisture. Generally these last traces of impurity can easily be removed by careful crystallization and then drying. Occasionally, sublimation (see Chapter 9) or distillation (see Chapter 11) is preferable.

The quantities of purified material usually required for microanalyses are:

C and H	3–4 mg (semi-micro, 10–12 mg)
N and O	3–8 mg
S, halogen, OMe and NMe	3–10 mg
M (Rast)	1 mg (semi-micro, 5 mg)
Titration	1–10 mg
Ultraviolet or infra-red spectrum	1–200 mg

GENERAL PROCEDURE

A portion of the solid (500 mg, if possible) is recrystallized to constant melting point. When the compound has no characteristic melting point, some other physical property such as light absorption or optical rotation is used as a criterion of purity. The sample is then given a final crystallization, with special precautions to ensure removal of filter-paper fibres, etc. Samples of the purified solid are then dried in clean specimen tubes. Finally, the melting point of the dried compound is checked, and the tubes are stoppered or sealed and labelled.

MELTING POINT DETERMINATION

The melting point and sharpness of melting are widely used as tests of the purity of solid organic compounds. Traces of impurity other than inorganic salts usually depress the melting point (phase rule). Mixed m.pt determinations are useful for the identification of organic compounds and rarely fail. It is important to place all three capillaries (known and unknown compounds and the mixture) in the heating bath together.

Calibrate the thermometer, if this has not already been done, against a standardized one (National Physical Laboratory statement of examination). Mount the thermometer and the standard, side by side, in a bath of medicinal paraffin stirred mechanically. Raise the temperature at 2–3°/minute and note both thermometer readings at intervals of 5°. Tabulate the observations and plot the corrections ($\pm$) against temperature.

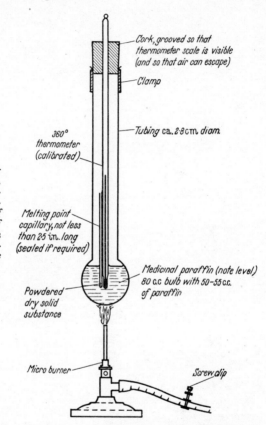

Cork, grooved so that thermometer scale is visible (and so that air can escape)

Clamp

Tubing ca. 2·8 cm. diam.

360° thermometer (calibrated)

Melting point capillary, not less than 2·5 in. long (sealed if required)

Medicinal paraffin (note level) 80 c.c bulb with 50–55 c.c. of paraffin

Powdered dry solid substance

Micro burner

Screw clip

Figure 26. Apparatus for melting point determination. Important points are : distance of micro-burner beneath paraffin bulb; level of paraffin in bulb; position of thermometer bulb; and length of m.pt capillary and position of contained substance

Take the m.pt of a 0·5-mg portion of the solid (m.pt < 300°) in a capillary, with the simple bulb apparatus containing medicinal paraffin (*Figure 26*) (*cf*. Film, 'How to take a melting point', Brent Laboratories, London). Control the micro-burner flame with a screw clip on the gas supply tubing, and raise the temperature of the paraffin at 10–20°/minute to 30° below the expected m.pt of the solid, and then at 2–3°/minute. Use a lens and note the temperature or range of melting, and whether decomposition, gas

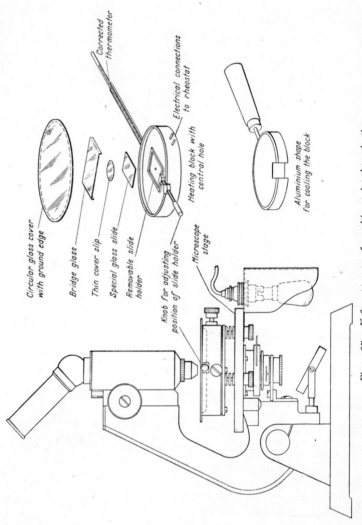

Figure 27. Kofler apparatus for melting point determination

evolution, resolidification on further heating, or sublimation occurs.

Make m.pt tubes by softening a cleaned, dried test-tube (5 × ⅜ in.) in a bunsen burner flame and pulling it out to a thin-walled capillary. Seal this off into 5-in. lengths with the aid of a micro-burner flame. Store the tubes in a clean bottle. Cut them in half, as required, with the sharp edge of a piece of broken tile.

Press out a little of the solid on a porous tile with a micro-spatula, to crush the crystals and to remove traces of solvent. Push *ca.* 0·5 mg of the powder into the open end of the m.pt capillary and tap it down to the closed end (it may be necessary to stroke the tube with a file). Touch the side of the m.pt tube against the thermometer bulb (which is covered with a film of liquid paraffin) and then place the m.pt tube against the thermometer with the enclosed substance level with the mercury bulb. Provided the m.pt tube is at least two inches long it will adhere firmly to the thermometer by capillarity. Then insert the thermometer into the bulb of medicinal paraffin as shown (*Figure 26*). Do not have more than 50–55 c.c. of medicinal paraffin (at room temperature) in an 80-c.c. bulb: the m.pt capillary will then be in no danger of falling off, even at 300°.

For melting points in the range 300–550° use an electric apparatus with a 550° nitrogen-filled mercury thermometer (Sugden Powell Ltd, London). Do not raise the temperature too rapidly.

For melting points on single crystals use an electrically heated block on a microscope stage, e.g. the Kofler apparatus (*Figure 27*) (C. Reichert, Vienna). Clean the special glass slide, place it in the movable holder and put one crystal on the slide over the central hole in the heater block. Cover the crystal with a cover-slip and put in position the bridge-glass and the circular glass cover of the heater block. Switch on the lamp and the heater, focus the microscope on to the crystal and control the rheostat so that near the m.pt the temperature rises at 1–2°/minute. Observe the temperature of melting. The special thermometer gives the corrected m.pt direct.

Remove (with forceps) the circular glass cover, the bridge-glass and the slide holder with slide, and place the thick aluminium shape on the block so as to cool it rapidly. Subsequently clean the special slide.

CRYSTALLIZATION OF THE SOLID TO CONSTANT MELTING POINT

Usually conditions are such that the required material separates in the first crops and impurities are left in the mother liquor. If, however, the solid is contaminated with sparingly soluble impurity, the first small crop must be rejected at each crystallization.

Use 1–2-mg portions of the solid in small test-tubes (e.g. 3 × ⅜ in.) and find a solvent or mixture of solvents from which the solid crystallizes readily: make notes. Then crystallize a 0·5-g portion to constant m.pt using test-tubes ($5 \times \frac{5}{8}$ in.) or small conical flasks; first treat coloured materials with charcoal (see below). If the purity of the compound is still suspect, crystallize the compound again from a different solvent and check the m.pt.

USE OF CHARCOAL: ALTERNATIVE TO THE USUAL METHOD

Cover a paper disc in a Hirsch funnel with a layer (2–3 mm thick) of kieselguhr ('acid-washed', British Drug Houses Ltd), (or filter aid) and then a layer of charcoal (see *Figure 28*). For example, for

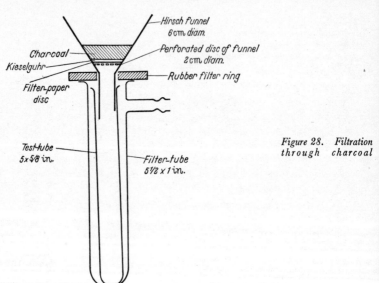

Figure 28. Filtration through charcoal

20 c.c. of solution use a funnel with a 2–3-cm diameter plate and have the charcoal about 1 cm thick. Press the materials down, run some hot solvent through, change the receiver, filter the hot, coloured solution, and finally give the filter-bed a wash with 2–3 c.c. of the hot solvent. (This method is efficient and minimizes losses.)

FINAL CRYSTALLIZATION FOR ANALYSIS

Brush the crystallization apparatus (test-tubes or small conical flasks) and filtration apparatus (small glass funnel, or funnel with sintered-glass filter-plate) under the tap and wash it with hot chromic–sulphuric acid cleaning mixture and with distilled water.

Dry the apparatus in a clean oven, or by rinsing it with redistilled ethanol and then redistilled dry ether.

Filter the hot solution of the compound *under gravity* through a clean fluted filter-paper in the glass funnel, preheated if necessary. Alternatively, filter the solution through the sintered-glass filter with suction (*Figure 29* shows sintered-glass filters for hot and cold

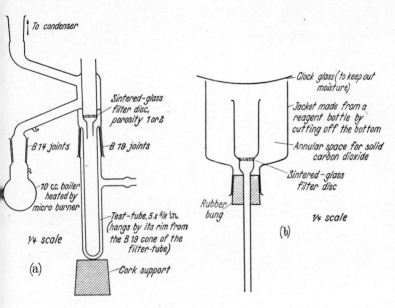

Figure 29. Jacketed sintered-glass filters for (a) hot, (b) cold filtrations

filtrations). Either collect the filtrate directly in a clean test-tube, or transfer it to a small conical flask. Stopper the vessel with a cellophane-covered cork (arrange the cellophane to prevent dust from settling on the rim of the vessel), and cool the vessel in ice-water to induce rapid formation of small crystals.

Break up the mass of crystals in the vessel with a clean spatula, and transfer, with gentle swirling, the slurry of crystals and mother liquor to a suction filter. Small quantities of crystals and liquor are best transferred on to a micro-filter with a clean dropper which has a wider nozzle than for the manipulation of liquids (see *Figure 33*). Interrupt the suction each time the liquid drains through the filter so that the mother liquor which still moistens the mass of crystals is not evaporated to dryness. Rinse the flask with a little of the *cold* solvent or mixture of solvents and run the rinsings through the filter. Wash the mass of crystals once more with fresh, cold solvent. When the solvent has a high boiling point, wash the solid again with a volatile miscible solvent in which the solid is not appreciably soluble. Place a glass cover over the filter-funnel, and drain the crystals under suction, for 15–30 seconds only to avoid their contamination with atmospheric dust. Either leave the crystals, covered, to air-dry for a few minutes, or place the funnel and contents in a desiccator. Check the melting point of the purified solid.

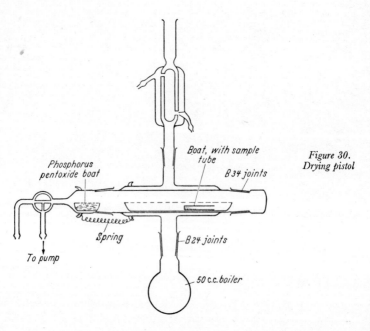

Figure 30.
Drying pistol

DRYING AND BOTTLING OF THE PURIFIED SAMPLE

The purification of solid compounds is completed by a drying process: this removes all traces of solvent, some of which may be occluded within the crystal lattice.

Carefully clean and dry two specimen tubes (e.g. $2 \times \frac{3}{8}$ in.), and transfer the purified solid to them with a micro-spatula. Do not scrape the filter-paper or sintered-glass disc. If the quantity of the solid is very small, lift the filter-paper out of the funnel with forceps and tap the paper gently inside the specimen tube so that the solid falls off, free from paper-fibres.

Dry the specimen tubes and their contents for 1 hour in a drying pistol (see *Figure 30*) connected to the filter-pump. Usually water (b.pt 100°) or acetone (b.pt 56°) is refluxed in the boiler (the temperature should be at least 30° below the m.pt of the substance). Place a boat of fresh phosphorus pentoxide at the cold vacuum-connection end of the apparatus and place the specimen tubes with their open ends pointed away from that end.

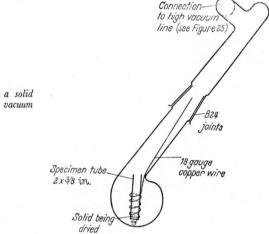

Figure 31. Drying a solid sample in a high vacuum

Alternatively, mount the specimen tubes in spiral wire holders in a vacuum retort (*Figure 31*) and dry the samples at 10^{-4} mm of mercury or less for 1–2 hours. Gentle heat can be applied (electric furnace at 50°) but is usually unnecessary and may cause sublimation.

Dry heat-sensitive compounds over concentrated sulphuric acid or phosphorus pentoxide in a vacuum desiccator overnight. If the solid is volatile, dry it over a desiccant in a small desiccator at atmospheric pressure.

When admitting air to an evacuated drying pistol or desiccator hold a piece of filter-paper against the tap nozzle to prevent too rapid a rush of air into the apparatus.

Determine the melting point of the substance after the drying, to ascertain that no chemical change such as loss of hydrochloric acid from a hydrochloride, loss of solvent from a solvate, decarboxylation of an acid, etc., has occurred.

Stopper the specimen tubes with cellophane-covered corks (or seal them) and label the tubes. Keep one sample for reference and use the other for analysis.

A recent, excellent innovation is polythene stoppers for small specimen tubes (Johsen and Jorgensen Flint Glass Ltd., London.)

11

FINAL PURIFICATION OF LIQUIDS
FOR ANALYSIS

AND A NOTE ON SMALL-SCALE MOLECULAR
DISTILLATION

INTRODUCTION (*cf.* Chapter 10)

THE most likely trace contaminants of a substantially pure liquid organic compound are dissolved moisture (from glassware), solvents and tap-grease. Usually the liquid can be brought to analytical purity by careful fractional distillation. The apparatus is designed to prevent the liquid distillate from coming into contact with rubber, or greased taps and ground-glass joints.

GENERAL PROCEDURE

The liquid is fractionally distilled, if necessary under reduced pressure, in cleaned and dried apparatus until the boiling point and the refractive index of the main fraction become constant. Samples of the purified liquid are sealed in clean, dry ampoules.

DETERMINATION OF THE REFRACTIVE INDEX

The refractive index of a liquid is usually a better criterion of purity than the boiling point. With either daylight or artificial light, the Abbe refractometer (see *Figure 32*) (Hilger and Watts Ltd, London) gives values of refractive index (to 4 decimal places) with respect to the sodium D line, i.e. n_D^t, where t is the temperature of the liquid in °C. Approximately, a rise in temperature of 1° makes a decrease of 0·0004 in the refractive index.

Determine the refractive index of the liquid organic compound. Use the Abbe refractometer carefully: it is a costly precision instrument. If readings other than at room temperature are required, pass water from a circulating thermostat (e.g. see *Figure 89*) through the prism block for at least 15 minutes.

Introduce a film of the liquid between the prism surfaces, *without touching and scratching them*, as follows. Open the prism block, place a drop of the liquid on the lower prism surface *b* (*Figure 32*) with a dropper (*Figure 33*), and close the prism block, at the same time tilting the instrument momentarily so that the liquid does not run off the prism. Alternatively, open the prism block slightly, run a drop of the liquid from the dropper into the groove *a* at the side of the block and close the prism block again.

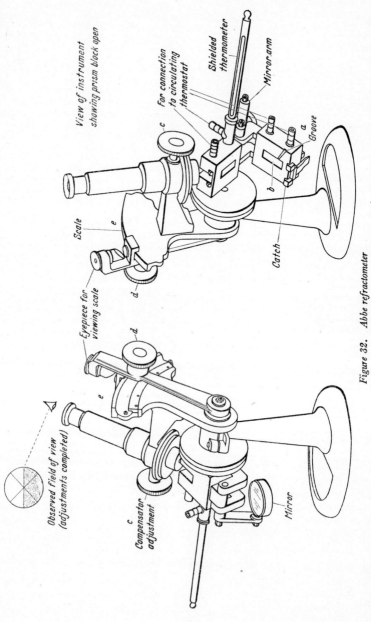

Figure 32. Abbe refractometer

Adjust the mirror, for good illumination, and turn the main knob *d* of the instrument until the field of view is partly dark. Adjust the compensator *c* until the edge of the dark field is sharp, and then turn the main knob *d* until this edge is coincident with the intersection of the eyepiece cross-wires. Read the scale *e*.

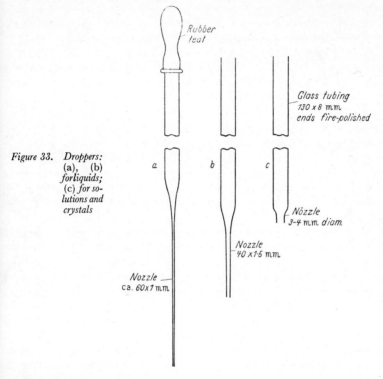

Figure 33. Droppers: (a), (b) for liquids; (c) for solutions and crystals

Take further readings, as a check, by approaching the intersection point alternately from the top and the bottom of the field of view. Note the prism temperature.

Clean both prism surfaces with cotton-wool moistened with a volatile solvent and then with dry cotton-wool. Avoid spilling liquid on the hinge of the prism block.

BOILING POINT DETERMINATION (MICRO)

The method is rapid and accurate to ± 10°.

Draw off one end of an open m.pt tube (p 57) in a very small micro-burner flame to a fine capillary and break this off 5–10 mm from the main part of the tube (see *Figure 34*). Insert the capillary tip into the liquid, momentarily, and then seal off the capillary in the micro-burner flame. (Ignition of some of the liquid during this operation does not matter.) Place the tube against the thermo-meter in the bulb, as shown in *Figure 34*, and slowly raise the temperature of the oil. The meniscus of the liquid in the capillary disappears from view at the boiling point. Note the temperature and whether the liquid decomposes.

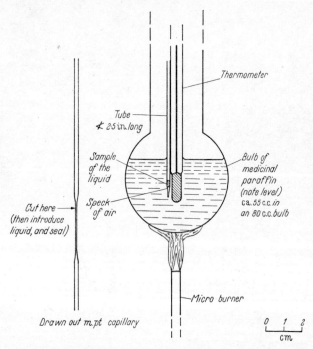

Figure 34. Micro method for boiling point determination (c.f. Figure 26)

FRACTIONAL DISTILLATION OF A LIQUID (WITH B.PT < 300°) FOR ANALYSIS

Fractionally distil a portion (2–5 c.c.) of the liquid in a small apparatus (5- or 15-c.c. flask) with multiple tube receiver (*Figure 35*), either at atmospheric pressure if the liquid is stable and has b.pt < 150–200°, or under controlled reduced pressure.

Clean the selected apparatus chemically and dry it (see p 58). Run the organic liquid into the flask until it is one-third full, and

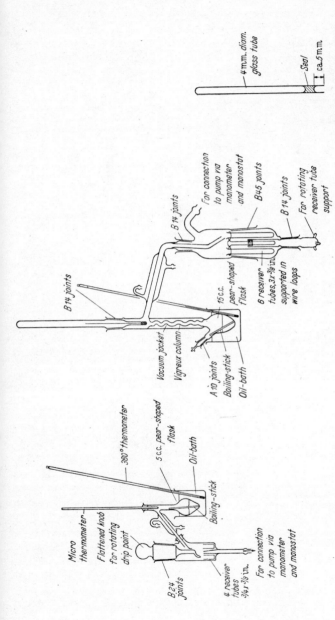

Figure 36. *Anti-bumping tube, e.g. 80 mm. long for a 250-c.c. flask*

4 mm. diam. glass tube
Seal
ca. 5 mm.

B 14 joints

For connection to pump via manometer and manostat

B 45 joints

B 14 joints

For rotating receiver tube support

Vacuum jacket
Vigreux column

15 c.c. pean-shaped flask

6 receiver tubes, 3 × 3/8 in. supported in wire loops

A 10 joints
Boiling-stick
Oil-bath

Figure 35. *Small-scale distillation apparatus*

Micro thermometer
Flattened knob for rotating drip point
360° thermometer
5 c.c. pean-shaped flask
Oil-bath
Boiling-stick
B 24 joints
4 receiver tubes 3/4 × 3/8 in.
For connection to pump via manometer and manostat

add 2–3 fragments of porous pot and an anti-bumping tube (*Figure 36*) or boiling-stick (wooden applicators, plain, round type, 6 in. long, Medical Supply Association, London) to promote smooth ebullition irrespective of the pressure. Assemble the apparatus and, if necessary, connect it to the source of vacuum (filter-pump or mechanical pump) via a manometer and a manostat in that order.

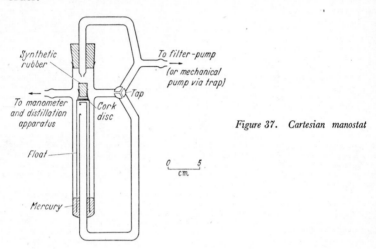

Figure 37. Cartesian manostat

A simple Cartesian manostat for control of pressure in the range 1–760 mm of mercury is shown in *Figure 37* (W. Edwards and Co. Ltd). Turn off the manostat tap when the pressure, indicated by the manometer, has fallen to the required value. Air is thereby enclosed in the float at that pressure and any tendency for the pressure in the attached distillation system to vary from that value, causes the float to move and either open or close the connection to the pump.

Vertical manometers are simplest and cover the range 5–760 mm. The compact type, shown in *Figure 38*(a), which covers the range 1–100 mm has advantages over the closed-limb U-tube type in that it is easier to clean and to fill and cannot be damaged by sudden admission of air. For the range 1–10^{-2} mm use the compact pattern of McLeod gauge, e.g. the Edwards 'Vacustat' [*Figure 38* (b)]. Normally the gauge is kept in the 'resting' position, evacuated, and with the tap closed. To measure the pressure in a (connected) vacuum system, open the tap, wait 30 seconds and then turn the gauge to the upright 'reading' position. Read

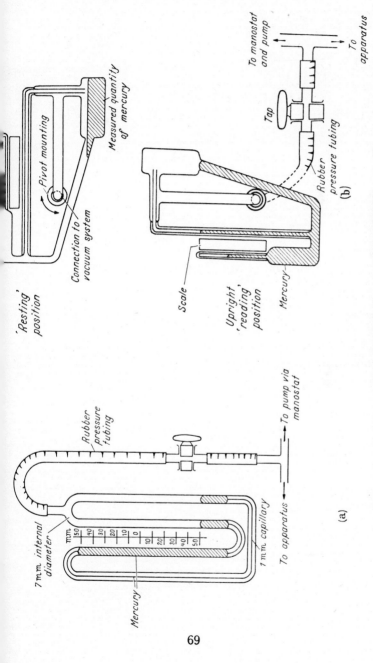

Figure 38. (a) *Manometer for measurement of pressures in range 1–100 mm; Hg*
(b) *'Vacustat' for measurement of pressures in range 10^{-2}–1 mm; Hg*

the position of the mercury in the closed limb on the attached scale: this gives the pressure in mm of mercury. Turn the gauge back to the 'resting' position and close the tap.

Heat the distillation flask in an oil-bath to 10–30° above the boiling point of the liquid so as to obtain a fairly slow, uniform rate of distillation. Reject the first and last few drops of distillate and collect 3–4 intermediate fractions. Note their boiling points and the pressure, and subsequently determine their refractive indices (n_D^t). After a reduced-pressure fractionation, open the tap of the manostat before admitting (dry) air cautiously to the apparatus. Do not expose the liquid fractions to the atmosphere unduly. Clean and dry the apparatus. Combine fractions

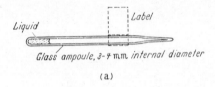

(a)

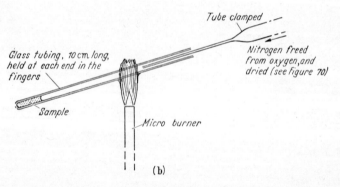

(b)

Figure 39. (a) *Ampoule for samples of liquids ;* (b) *method of sealing a sample under nitrogen*

which have close boiling points and/or refractive indices (differences in n_D of 1 unit or more at the third decimal place are significant), transferring the liquid with a clean dropper (*Figure 33*). In the same manner, refractionate the main fraction, until a sample is obtained with a constant boiling point and refractive index. At once seal the required number of samples of the purified liquid in ampoules (see below).

SEALING OF LIQUID SAMPLES FOR ANALYSIS *(Figure 39)*

Seal one end of a 10-cm length of chemically clean, dried, glass tubing (3–4 mm internal diameter): *do not blow into it.* Allow the glass to cool, and introduce the purified liquid (say, 10–50 mg)

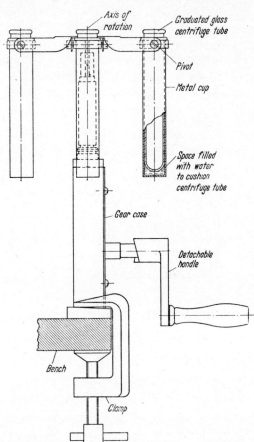

Figure 40. Hand centrifuge

by means of a clean dry capillary dropper (*Figure 33*). Centrifuge the liquid to the bottom of the tube by a few turns in the hand centrifuge (*Figure 40*) (A. Gallenkamp and Co. Ltd, London), and then draw off the open end of the tube in a micro-burner flame to a stout capillary seal [see *Figure 39*(a)]. Label the ampoule.

The method of sealing a sample under nitrogen is indicated in *Figure 39*(b). First displace the air in the ampoule with purified dried nitrogen (p 139 and *Figure 70*). Then soften the glass in a small hot flame as shown, allow it to collapse and seal off the ampoule by drawing away the lower part of the tube.

NOTE ON SMALL-SCALE MOLECULAR DISTILLATION

(*cf.* CARNEY, *Laboratory Fractional Distillation*, The Macmillan Company, New York, 1949, Chapter 22.)

Small quantities of very high boiling organic liquids and syrups or glasses can be distilled molecularly under high vacuum from heated retorts. A retort (15 c.c.) with a side arm and a 4-tube fraction collector is shown in *Figure 41*.

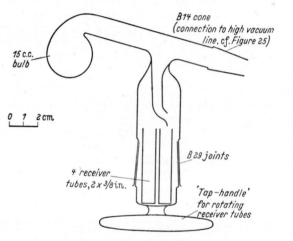

Figure 41. Retort, with receiver, for the distillation of high boiling oils

With a sufficiently low pressure (10^{-5}–10^{-8} mm) and at moderate temperatures (50–300°) the mean free path of the molecules which escape from the liquid surface will be greater than the distance from that surface to the 'cold' receiver (i.e. neck of the retort). The liquid remains quiescent and distillate slowly collects in the neck of the retort. Since the neck will be warm because of its proximity to the electric furnace, even viscous distillates flow fairly readily into the fraction collector.

Viscous materials are best introduced into a retort as solutions in volatile solvents. The solution is poured through a thistle funnel into the bulb, and the solvent is then evaporated off under filter-pump vacuum whilst the retort is heated by being swirled

72

gently over the steam-bath (*cf. Figure 52*). Further portions of the solution can be added and evaporated until the bulb is about one-third filled with the oil or 'glass'. The retort, still connected to the filter-pump, is then heated (with the neck uppermost) in the steam-bath for 15–30 minutes to ensure the complete removal of the solvent. Only then may the retort be connected to the high vacuum system.

PART II

SPECIAL REACTION TECHNIQUES

12

VACUUM-LINE TECHNIQUE

THE vacuum-line method is unsurpassed for the manipulation of gases and volatile liquids, particularly on the small scale and when these are valuable, noxious, or radioactive. The apparatus consists of a length of wide-bore tubing (the manifold), along which there are side tubes (with taps) for the connection of reaction vessels, etc. (see *Figure 44*). The end of the manifold leads through a cold trap to an efficient pumping system. The degree of vacuum attained directly affects the efficiency with which materials can be transferred from one vessel to another by vaporization and condensation.

Small quantities of volatile liquids are best measured as vapour. Thus 0·5 c.c. of liquid methyl iodide would be difficult to measure accurately by volume or weight, and transfer losses would be considerable. However, as a gas at 20°, occupying e.g. 735 c.c. it would exert a pressure of 200 mm of mercury, and this could be read on a simple manometer to 0·5 per cent or better. The procedure for measuring a volatile liquid is, then, to vaporize the liquid into an evacuated vessel of known volume until the pressure reached (at the prevailing temperature) is that which corresponds to the required weight of the compound. An alcohol–solid carbon dioxide bath will condense the vapour (e.g. methyl iodide) to liquid again at the required point in the apparatus almost quantitatively, provided the system has previously been pumped as free as possible of non-condensable gas (i.e. air).

REFERENCES

CALVIN, HEIDELBERGER, REID, TOLBERT and YANKWICH, *Isotopic Carbon*, Chapman and Hall, Ltd, London, 1949.

FARKAS and MELVILLE, *Experimental Methods in Gas Reactions*, Macmillan and Co. Ltd, London, 1939.

JNANANANDA, *High Vacua*, Van Nostrand and Co., London, 1947.

KAMEN, *Radio-active Tracers in Biology*, Vol. I, Academic Press Inc., New York, 1947.

REIMANN, *Vacuum Technique*, Chapman and Hall, Ltd, London, 1952.

STRONG, *Procedures in Experimental Physics*, Prentice-Hall, Inc., New York, 1944.

YARWOOD, *High Vacuum Technique*, Chapman and Hall, Ltd, London, 1948.

HIGH-VACUUM PUMPING SYSTEM

The essentials of a high-vacuum pumping system, of which there are many possible modifications, are shown in *Figure 42*. A mechanical 'backing' pump is connected through a special tap *a* to an oil or a mercury diffusion (ejection) pump, in turn connected

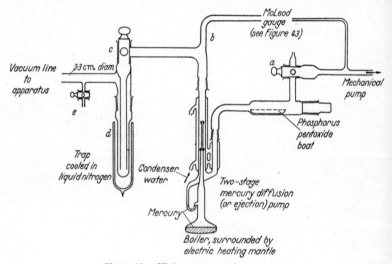

Figure 42. High-vacuum pumping system

via a tap *c*, a liquid-nitrogen cooled trap *d* and the line to the apparatus. Tap *a* connects the pump to the air or to the diffusion pump but not the diffusion pump to the air. The pressure gauge (Pirani or ionization, for pressures $< 10^{-5}$ mm of mercury, or McLeod, for 10^{-5}–10^{-2} mm) is attached at *b*.

Operation

On a cold day, before attempting to turn the taps of the system warm them *slightly* with warm air from the blower, to soften the grease. Check that the taps and joints are correctly greased (see p 80).

Tap *c* should already be closed. Switch on the mechanical pump and turn tap *a* to connect the mechanical with the diffusion pump. Switch on the heater of the diffusion pump and turn on the water to the condenser. Make sure the trap at *d* is clean and dry. Connect the apparatus to the line, close tap *e*, open tap *c* slowly and, after a few minutes, put the Dewar flask of liquid nitrogen in place at *d*.

Read the pressure gauge when the system is fully evacuated, i.e. after the diffusion pump has been operating fully for 15 minutes.

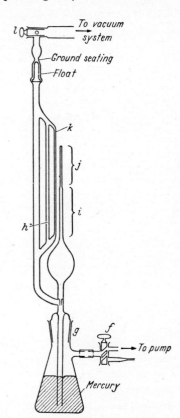

Figure 43. McLeod gauge for measurement of pressures in range 10^{-5}–10^{-2} *mm Hg*

The McLeod gauge (Figure 43) (J. W. Towers and Co. Ltd, Widnes) —(If the gauge is not under vacuum, evacuate the flask *g* and the upper part of the gauge simultaneously through taps *f* and *l*.) Open tap *l* to the vacuum system and after 1–2 minutes turn tap *f* to admit air *very slowly* to the flask *g*. The mercury then rises in the apparatus, and will reach a level in the reservoir at either *i* or *j.* Close the tap *f*, when the mercury in either *h* (with mercury at *i*) or *k* (with mercury at *j*) is level with the top end of the reservoir capillary (at *j*). Read the position of the mercury in the reservoir (at *i* or *j*) on the attached scale: this gives the pressure in the system connected at *l*. To reset the gauge, close tap *l*, open tap *f* to the pump and evacuate the flask *g*. Close the tap *f*.

To close down the vacuum system
Close tap *c* and switch off the diffusion pump heater. Open tap *a* to the air and switch off the mechanical pump. Open tap *e* to the air and remove the Dewar flask of liquid nitrogen from *d*. Turn off the condenser water. When the trap at *d* has warmed to room temperature, remove it, clean and dry it and regrease the joint (see below). Replace the trap at *d*.

PREPARATION OF CARBOXYL-LABELLED ACETIC ACID

The reactions are:

$$\overset{*}{BaCO_3} \xrightarrow[\;(a)\;]{H_2SO_4} \overset{*}{CO_2} \xrightarrow[\;(b)\;]{MeMgI} Me{\cdot}\overset{*}{CO_2}MgI \xrightarrow[\;(c)\;]{H_2SO_4} Me{\cdot}\overset{*}{CO_2}H$$

The procedures in this experiment give the maximum practice in gas handling. Normally, with $[^{14}C]O_2$, the Grignard reagent is used in excess.

Preliminaries
As shown in *Figure 44*, fit reaction vessels to the vacuum manifold (supported on a metal-rod framework, e.g. 'Keeklamp' scaffolding, Griffin and George Ltd, London, or 'Lablox' scaffolding, J. W. Towers Ltd, Widnes); make sure that all the joints and taps are correctly greased and fit the safety springs.

Greasing of taps—Clean the tap barrel and the socket with cotton-wool moistened with benzene. Warm the barrel and socket gently with a flame and apply the grease ('Apiezon M') as a few light *longitudinal* streaks. Insert the barrel into its socket and twist the barrel backwards and forwards several times (the procedure prevents bubbles of air being occluded in the grease).

Greasing of joints—Clean and warm both halves of the joint and apply the grease to the cone or ball half of the joint, as for the tap barrel, above. Then twist the two halves of the joint together.

(a) *Generation of carbon dioxide* (see *Figure 44*)
Place concentrated sulphuric acid (20 c.c.) in the pressure-equalized dropping funnel *c* with tap *b′* closed and barium carbonate (assumed

to be $Ba[^{14}C]O_3$) in the 100-c.c. flask d. The carbon dioxide storage bulb f has a capacity of 2 litres. Hence for safety, do not generate more than 1–1·5 litre of carbon dioxide (at s.t.p.), so that the pressure in the bulb f will be less than atmospheric. *Calculate the quantity of barium carbonate.*

With taps a, b, ϵ and e' open (and the others closed), pump out the apparatus as completely as possible. Read the McLeod gauge (see above) and the manometer h. Close tap a.

Immerse the tip of the bulb f in liquid nitrogen contained in the Dewar flask at g, and open tap b' slightly to admit sulphuric acid to d so as to generate carbon dioxide slowly. Finally, warm the flask d to complete the reaction (barium sulphate is appreciably soluble in hot concentrated sulphuric acid), and raise the Dewar flask at g to ensure that the carbon dioxide is all condensed in the tip of the bulb f. Close taps b' and b.

Remove the Dewar flask at g, and, when the carbon dioxide in f has evaporated, check the pressure at h. Gradually immerse the tip of the bulb f in liquid nitrogen to recondense the carbon dioxide. Close tap e'.

At this stage, the line and the generator which is attached at b can be flushed free from traces of the radioactive carbon dioxide. This is done by pumping with taps a and b open, admitting air through a, and repumping. The exhaust is led outside the building. Finally, air is admitted to the line through a, and the generator can then safely be detached. (If desired, the bulb of carbon dioxide can also be detached from the line: tap e is then closed.) Tap b is closed and the manifold evacuated once again: the pressure is then checked with the McLeod gauge.

(b) *Preparation and carboxylation of the Grignard reagent*

Place magnesium turnings (0·50 g; dried for 10 minutes in the oven) in the flask l, and add ether (50 c.c., sodium-dried). Place methyl iodide in the graduated tube j. Cautiously immerse j and l in liquid nitrogen and evacuate them through taps i, i' and k, k' respectively. Then close tap a. Allow the contents of the tube j to thaw, and warm the tube j gently with the hand until 1 c.c. (2·28 g) of methyl iodide has distilled into the flask l (accurate measurement is unnecessary here). Close taps i, i', k and k' and allow the contents of the flask l to thaw. Place solid carbon dioxide and alcohol in the condenser m, immerse the flask l in a brine-bath at room temperature and stir the contents of the flask l magnetically whilst the ether refluxes. When formation of the Grignard reagent is complete, cool the flask l to $-20°$ with alcohol and solid carbon dioxide (use a pentane thermometer), and, by opening the taps k', k, e and e', introduce the carbon dioxide contained in the bulb f.

81

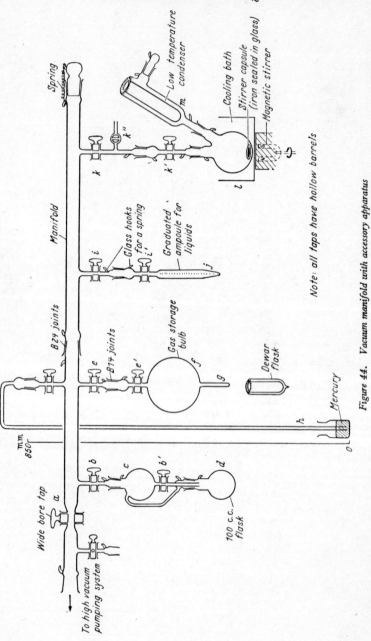

Figure 44. *Vacuum manifold with accessory apparatus*

82

Maintain vigorous stirring in the flask l to prevent the reaction mixture from setting to a gel, and keep the temperature at $-20°$.

After 30 minutes, condense the excess of carbon dioxide in the bulb f, by immersing the tip once more in liquid nitrogen. Close tap e'. Admit air to the system through a (via the cold trap) and then pump it out again (exhaust outside the building), in order to flush the last traces of radioactive carbon dioxide from the manifold and the flask l.

(c) *Isolation of the acetic acid as sodium acetate*

Solid or liquid [^{14}C] compounds or their solutions must be manipulated with care, and contamination of the hands, etc., must be avoided scrupulously. Filtrations, transfer operations, etc., must therefore be performed quantitatively.

Close tap k, open k'' and remove the flask l from the line.

In the fume-chamber, treat the contents of the flask, still at $-20°$, with 6N-sulphuric acid (15 c.c.). Add water (35 c.c.) and then silver sulphate (3·25 g) to remove iodine. Distil off the ether, and steam-distil the residue until 300 c.c. have been collected. Then treat the aqueous solution of the acetic acid with 1 equivalent of approximately 0·1N-sodium hydroxide; determine the end-point with the aid of a pH meter.

Place the electrodes of the pH meter (see Chapter 25) in aqueous sodium acetate (*ca.* 0·3 per cent) and set the meter to an arbitrary reading (e.g. pH 8·0). Rinse the electrodes with distilled water and immerse them in the solution of acetic acid. Then titrate the acetic acid with approximately 0·1N-sodium hydroxide until the pH meter reading returns to the arbitrary setting.

Distil the solution to small bulk (10–15 c.c.), add charcoal, filter, and evaporate it to dryness under reduced pressure in a tared specimen-flask. Record the yield of sodium acetate (*ca.* 1 g).

Disposal of waste solids and solutions which may have become radioactive (e.g. the charcoal, and the residue from the steam-distillation) must be carried out in accordance with the laboratory regulations.

13

CATALYTIC HYDROGENATION AT ATMOSPHERIC PRESSURE

INTRODUCTION

THE direct addition of hydrogen to olefinic and acetylenic linkages and the reduction with hydrogen of some unsaturated functional groups (e.g. $-NO_2 \rightarrow -NH_2$, $-CN \rightarrow -CH_2 \cdot NH_2$, $-CH{=}NOH \rightarrow -CH_2 \cdot NH_2$, $-N{=}N- \rightarrow 2NH_2$) can be effected catalytically at ordinary temperature and pressure. A solution of the compound in, for example, water, ethanol, acetic acid or ethyl acetate is shaken with hydrogen gas in the presence of platinum, palladium or Raney catalysts.

REFERENCES

BERKMAN, MORRELL and EGLOFF, *Catalysis*, Reinhold Publishing Corpn, New York, 1940.

FRANKENBURG, KOMAREWSKY and RIDEAL, *Advances in Catalysis, and Related Subjects*, Academic Press Inc., New York, 1952, Vol. IV, and previous volumes.

GILMAN, *Organic Chemistry*, John Wiley and Sons, Inc., New York, 1947, Vol. I, Chapter 9.

JOHNSON, *Sci. Progr. Twent. Cent.*, 1949, **37**, 512.

THORPE and WHITELEY, *Thorpe's Dictionary of Applied Chemistry*, Longmans, Green and Co., London, 1943, Vol. VI, p 347.

CATALYSTS

Prepare one of the following:

(a) *Adams's catalyst* ($PtO_2 \cdot H_2O$)

(*cf. Org. Synth.*, 1941, Coll. Vol. I, 463.)

The first part of this preparation must be performed in the fume-chamber.

Dissolve platinum chloride ($H_2PtCl_6 \cdot 6H_2O$; 1 g) in water (*ca.* 3 c.c.) in a porcelain crucible (3–4 cm diameter). Add sodium nitrate (10 g) and evaporate the mixture to dryness over a low flame, with continuous stirring. Then turn the bunsen burner full on, and stir the contents of the crucible vigorously until the mass has melted completely and the initial decomposition has subsided. Keep the bottom of the crucible at a dull red heat for a further 30 minutes (too strong a heat decomposes the platinum oxide to the metal). Allow the crucible to cool and wash the contents into a 400-c.c. beaker with hot water from a wash bottle. Filter off the brown platinum oxide on a Hirsch funnel (Whatman filter-paper, No. 541) and wash the oxide with hot water (about 1 litre) until the washings are free from nitrate ion. Dry the catalyst over calcium chloride in a vacuum desiccator.

(b) *Palladium black*

(*cf.* WIELAND, *Ber. dtsch. chem. Ges.*, 1912, **45**, 484.)

Heat a mixture of palladium chloride (1 g) and water (200 c.c.) to 80° and carefully *neutralize* it to wide-range indicator paper with 20 per cent sodium hydroxide solution. (If the end-point is over-shot, palladium hydroxide precipitates.) Add 2·6 per cent formic acid (5 c.c.) and after about 2 minutes make the solution strongly alkaline with 20 per cent sodium hydroxide solution (10 c.c.). Add more of the formic acid (10 c.c.) and make sure that the solution is still alkaline. Heat the mixture on the steam-bath for 2 hours. Filter off the precipitate on a Hirsch funnel (Whatman filter-paper, No. 541), wash it free from alkali, and dry it over calcium chloride in a vacuum desiccator.

(c) *Palladized charcoal* (5 per cent Pd)

(*cf.* VOGEL, *A Textbook of Practical Organic Chemistry*, Longmans, Green and Co., London, 1948, p 989.)

Heat decolorizing charcoal (15 g) on the steam-bath for 2–3 hours with concentrated hydrochloric acid (10 c.c.) and water (300 c.c.). Wash the charcoal by decantation with hot water until free from acid, filter it off, and dry it in the steam-oven.

Warm palladium chloride (1 g) in concentrated hydrochloric acid (1·5 c.c.) and water (10 c.c.) on the steam-bath for about 20 minutes. Add the solution to 'AnalaR' sodium acetate (35 g) in water (100 c.c.) contained in a hydrogenation flask. Introduce the purified charcoal (11·5 g) and hydrogenate the mixture until no more hydrogen is absorbed (about 2 hours). The hydrogenation procedure is described below. Collect the catalyst on a 7-cm Buchner filter (3 thicknesses of Whatman filter-paper, No. 1), wash it with water (5 × 100 c.c.), and drain it on the filter with suction. Dry the catalyst over fresh silica gel in a vacuum desiccator, and store it in a tightly stoppered bottle.

(d) *Palladized strontium carbonate* (2 per cent Pd)

(*cf.* BUSCH and STÖVE, *Ber. dtsch. chem. Ges.*, 1916, **49**, 1064; MARTIN and ROBINSON, *J. chem. Soc.*, **1943**, 491.)

Suspend powdered strontium carbonate (30 g) in water (300 c.c.) at 70°. Add palladium chloride (1 g) in warm concentrated hydrochloric acid (about 5 c.c.) and stir the mixture at 70° for 5–10 minutes. Filter off the catalyst on a 7-cm Buchner filter (3 thicknesses of Whatman filter-paper, No. 30), wash it thoroughly with hot water (about 1 litre) and dry it in the steam-oven.

HYDROGENATION OF MALEIC ACID

$$HO_2C\,CH\colon CH\cdot CO_2H + H_2 \rightarrow HO_2C\cdot CH_2\cdot CH_2\cdot CO_2H$$

Dissolve maleic acid (3 g) in ethanol (40 c.c.) in a hydrogenation flask (250 c.c.), and add the catalyst (20 mg of Adams's catalyst, 30 mg of palladium black, 100 mg of palladized charcoal, or 150 mg of palladized strontium carbonate).

Calculate the expected uptake of hydrogen. The burettes will need to be refilled during the experiment if their capacity is less than the theoretical uptake.

Hydrogenation apparatus

(See *Figure 45*; a similar model is made by J. W. Towers and Co. Ltd.)

Preliminaries—Examine all the taps and ensure that they are properly greased (the greased parts should be free from striations) (see p 80) and make certain that the bores are free. Apply a thin smear of grease around the *upper part* of the cone *k*. (Do not attach the hydrogenation flask yet.)

See that there is sufficient clean water in the reservoirs attached to the burettes *f* and *i*. (Addition of a little copper sulphate prevents mould growths.)

Connect tap *b* to the water pump or other source of vacuum via a trap and a three-way tap.

Connect a hydrogen cylinder (fitted with a reducing valve) by pressure tubing to the apparatus at *a*. There is a mercury safety valve at *d*.

Procedure—

(*1*) Open tap *j*. Raise the reservoirs attached to the burettes, and fill the burettes with water up to the taps *e* and *h*. Close taps *e* and *h*. Lower the reservoirs.

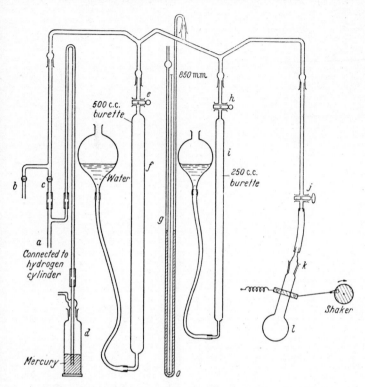

Figure 45. *Apparatus for catalytic hydrogenation at atmospheric pressure*

(2) Attach the hydrogenation flask (with contents) at *k* and fit the safety spring across the ground-glass joint.

(3) With tap *j* open, and taps *c*, *e* and *h* closed, evacuate the apparatus with a mechanical or filter-pump, via tap *b*.

(4) Close tap *b*, and fill the apparatus with hydrogen, via tap *c*, to atmospheric pressure (indicated on the manometer *g*). Close tap *c*.

(5) Re-evacuate the apparatus through tap *b* and then close *b*.

(6) Re-fill with hydrogen through tap *c*. Then open taps *e* and *h* so that the burettes fill with hydrogen. Close tap *c*.

(7) With taps *b* and *c* closed, and *e*, *h* and *j* open, level the water in the reservoirs against that in the burettes (to bring the hydrogen to atmospheric pressure). Note the water levels in the burettes. Close tap *h*.

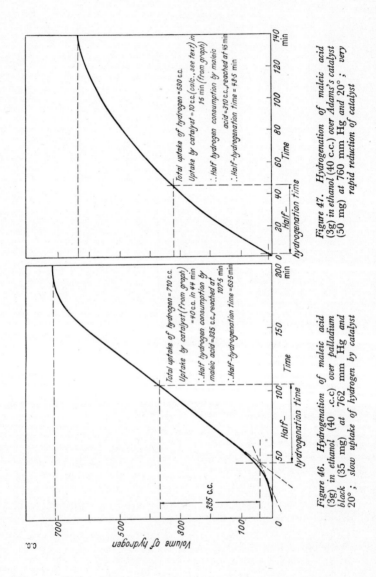

Figure 46. Hydrogenation of maleic acid (3g) in ethanol (40 .c.c) over palladium black (35 mg) at 762 mm Hg and 20°; slow uptake of hydrogen by catalyst

Total uptake of hydrogen = 710 c.c.
Uptake by catalyst (from graph) = 40 c.c. in 44 min
∴ Half hydrogen consumption by maleic acid = 335 c.c. reached at 107·5 min
∴ Half-hydrogenation time = 63·5 min

Figure 47. Hydrogenation of maleic acid (3g) in ethanol (40 c.c.) over Adams's catalyst (50 mg) at 760 mm Hg and 20°; very rapid reduction of catalyst

Total uptake of hydrogen = 630 c.c.
Uptake by catalyst = 10 c.c (calc., see text) in 1·5 min (from graph)
∴ Half hydrogen consumption by maleic acid = 310 c.c. reached at 45 min
∴ Half-hydrogenation time = 43·5 min

88

(8) Connect the hydrogenation flask l to the shaker. Switch on the shaker and from time to time adjust the level of the reservoir attached to the burette f so as to maintain the hydrogen at a pressure slightly greater than atmospheric. At intervals, level the water in the reservoir against that in the burette and note the reading. Plot the hydrogen uptake (in c.c.) against time (in minutes). When the hydrogen in f is almost used up, level off the reservoir, take the burette reading, and close tap e. Then open tap h and use the hydrogen in i.

(9) When absorption of hydrogen ceases, adjust the level of the reservoir for i and read the burette. Close tap h and switch off the shaker.

(10) With taps e and h closed, evacuate the apparatus through tap b. Admit air through b, and remove the flask l.

Filter off the catalyst through a thin layer of kieselguhr ('acid-washed') on a Hirsch funnel, wash it with a little alcohol, and place the catalyst with the filter-paper and filter-aid in the residue bottle. Evaporate the filtrate under reduced pressure and determine the weight (*ca.* 3 g) and melting point of the hydrogenation product, succinic acid (m.pt 185°). Recrystallize the acid from water, if necessary, and transfer the dried product to a labelled specimen tube.

Deduce from the graph (see *Figures 46* and *47*) the half-hydrogenation time (this is a measure of the activity of the catalyst) and the hydrogen uptake of the maleic acid at s.t.p., allowing for hydrogen absorption by the catalyst. The uptake by the palladium catalysts is obtained from the hydrogenation graph, and that for platinum oxide ($PtO_2 \cdot H_2O$) is calculated from the weight of the oxide.

Bottle and label the unused catalyst.

14

HIGH PRESSURE CATALYTIC HYDROGENATION

INTRODUCTION

CERTAIN types of catalytic reduction proceed readily under high hydrogen pressures, particularly at elevated temperatures, e.g.

Phenol → *cyclo*Hexanol ⎫ ············ ⎰ at 100°/100 atm over
Aniline → *cyclo*Hexylamine ⎭ ⎱ W–4 Raney nickel.
R·CO$_2$Et → R·CH$_2$OH ....at 200°/250 atm over
copper chromite.

There is, however, no strict division between those reductions which require high hydrogen pressures and those which proceed at ordinary pressure, since both the solvent and the catalyst can influence the speed, and sometimes the extent, of hydrogenation. The reduction of benzenoid rings (*cf.* above examples) can also be effected at ordinary pressure if a more active variety of the catalyst (W–6 or W–7) is used. Since these highly active nickel catalysts deteriorate rapidly, it is generally more convenient to use the moderately active W–4 catalyst and high hydrogen pressures.

REFERENCES

ADAMS, *Organic Reactions*, John Wiley and Sons, Inc., New York, 1954, Vol. VIII, Chapter 1.

BERKMAN, MORRELL and EGLOFF, *Catalysis*, Reinhold Publishing Corpn, New York, 1940.

FRANKENBURG, KOMAREWSKY and RIDEAL, *Advances in Catalysis, and Related Subjects*, Academic Press Inc., New York, 1952, Vol. IV, and previous volumes.

GILMAN, *Organic Chemistry*, John Wiley and Sons, Inc., New York, 1947, Vol. I, Chapter 9.

Newer Preparative Methods of Organic Chemistry, Interscience Publishers, Inc., New York, 1948, pp 61–123.

'W' numbers designate the activities of Raney nickel catalysts. See ADKINS and PAVLIC, *J. Amer. chem. Soc.*, 1947, **69**, 3039; *Org. Synth.*, 1949, **29**, 24; ADKINS and BILLICA, *J. Amer. chem. Soc.*, 1948, **70**, 695.

RANEY NICKEL CATALYST (W–4)

(*cf.* PAVLIC and ADKINS, *J. Amer. chem. Soc.*, 1946, **68**, 1471.)

Because of hydrogen evolution, remove all flames etc. from the vicinity of the apparatus.

Dissolve sodium hydroxide pellets (32·5 g) in water (125 c.c.) in a 500-c.c. three-necked flask, fitted with a mechanical stirrer and a thermometer. Mount the flask over a 12·5-cm funnel and cool the flask with running water (see *Figure 48*). When the temperature

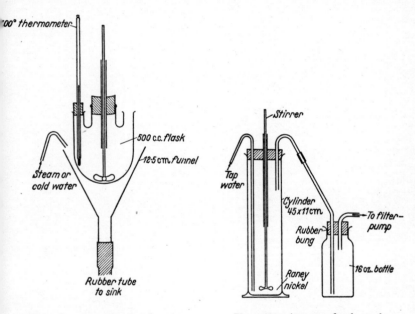

Figure 48. *Apparatus for the preparation of Raney nickel*

Figure 49. *Apparatus for the washing of Raney nickel*

of the solution has fallen to 50°, add Raney nickel alloy (25 g) in *small* portions (1–2 g) to the rapidly stirred solution to keep the temperature at 50° ± 2°. Control the foaming by adding a few drops of ethanol. When all the alloy has been added, keep the flask and contents at 50° for a further hour by passing steam into the funnel. Without further delay, wash the nickel by decantation with 2N-sodium hydroxide (100 c.c.) and then distilled water (2 × 100 c.c.); transfer the nickel to a 1-litre measuring cylinder, fitted with a stirrer. Pass tap water through a glass tube to the bottom of the cylinder at a rate of about 100 c.c./minute and draw off the overflow through a tube which just projects into the cylinder and is connected through a safety bottle to the water pump (see *Figure 49*). Adjust the rate of stirring so that the catalyst is churned

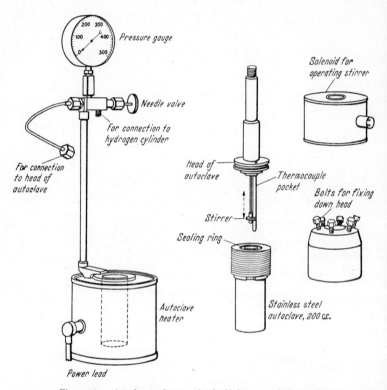

Figure 50. Autoclave and accessories for high pressure hydrogenation

about half-way up the cylinder (some fine particles will be carried over in the washings). After 1–1·5 hours, when the washings are neutral (wide-range indicator paper), allow the catalyst to settle and decant the water. Wash the nickel by decantation with ethanol (4 × 50 c.c.), and store the nickel under ethanol in a small wide-mouthed bottle. Allow a little of the catalyst to dry on a filter-paper: active catalysts inflame spontaneously.

Since the catalyst must be kept moist with solvent, transfer it from the stock bottle with a small spoon. If another solvent such as ethyl acetate, *cyclo*hexane, etc. is required for the hydrogenation, wash the catalyst by decantation several times with the new solvent before using it.

HYDROGENATION OF PHENOL OR ANILINE
(TO *cyclo*HEXANOL AND *cyclo*HEXYLAMINE RESPECTIVELY)

Add Raney nickel catalyst (*ca.* 4 g.; 1–2 teaspoonfuls) to a solution of phenol or aniline (20 g) in ethanol (100 c.c.) and put the mixture into the autoclave (e.g. 200-c.c. stainless steel type, Baskerville and Lindsay Ltd, Manchester) (see *Figure 50*), which is then sealed by the laboratory technician. Admit hydrogen to 100 atm pressure, and raise the temperature to 100°, having first calculated the expected rise in pressure as a routine precaution. Then start the stirrer. Calculate the expected uptake. With a good catalyst, absorption of hydrogen will be complete within 6 hours. A slower rate of uptake (poor quality catalyst) may be increased by raising the temperature to 120–150°. Note the drop in pressure and, when hydrogenation is complete, switch off the stirrer and the heater and allow the autoclave to cool before the excess of hydrogen is released. The autoclave is then opened by the technician. Wash the contents of the autoclave into a 500-c.c. beaker with a little ethanol. Clean and dry the autoclave and wipe the sealing ring with cotton-wool.

Remove the catalyst by filtering the reaction mixture through charcoal. Afterwards, wash the charcoal down the sink. Isolate the product from the filtrate by distillation through a vacuum-jacketed column (15 × 1·5 cm) packed with Fenske helices ($\frac{1}{8}$ in.). Record the yield, b.pt and refractive index of the product (*cyclo*-hexanol, b.pt 161°, m.pt 24°, *ca.* 15 g; *cyclo*hexylamine, b.pt 134°, *ca.* 15 g) together with the hydrogen uptake as molecular proportions (not moles). Without delay, transfer the product to a labelled bottle, or seal it in a specimen ampoule.

15

REACTION IN A CARIUS TUBE

For pressure reactions, metal autoclaves are generally available in laboratories. However, it is frequently more convenient, in small scale work ($\gtrless$ 50 c.c.), to use a thick-walled glass Carius tube. The reaction mixture will not then be in contact with metal; vitreous enamel-lined autoclaves are, of course, obtainable but they are expensive and easily damaged.

This experiment provides practice in the sealing and opening of Carius tubes and illustrates necessary precautions.

PREPARATION OF 1 : 3-Di-imino*iso*INDOLINE

(*cf*. ELVIDGE and LINSTEAD, *J. chem. Soc.*, **1952**, 5000.)

Ammonia is added, under pressure, to phthalonitrile.

(a) *Preliminaries*

Practise the sealing and opening operations (see below) on a length of empty tube.

Into a clean, dry Carius tube ($1 \cdot 5$ cm internal diameter, $\ngtr$ 50 cm long) introduce purified phthalonitrile (5 g) and then methanolic ammonia prepared (fume-chamber) by the cautious addition of liquid ammonia (run 10 c.c. from an upturned cylinder into a measuring cylinder) to stirred ice-cooled methanol (30 c.c.). Dry the inside of the open end of the Carius tube with a twist of filter-paper, and immerse the lower end in a 500-c.c. measuring cylinder containing ice and water.

(b) *Sealing, heating, and opening of the Carius tube*

Make certain that the blowpipe is connected to the gas, compressed air and oxygen supplies. Open the main valve on the

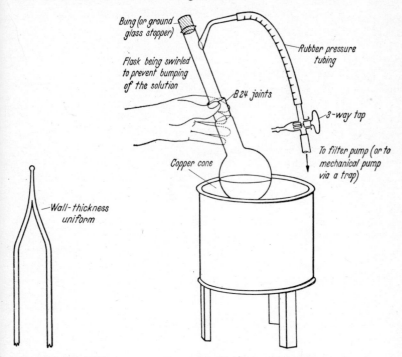

Figure 51.   Sealed end o̦
a Carius tube

Figure 52.   Evaporation of solutions under
reduced pressure on the steam-bath

oxygen cylinder, but not the diaphragm reducing valve (see p 117).
Keep the lower end of the Carius tube cooled, and seal the tube in
the following way.

Hold the Carius tube in the left hand and rotate the open end
in a large but not fierce, gas–air flame until the sodium-yellow just
appears.   Then turn on the oxygen so that the end of the Carius
tube is softened.   Meanwhile, using the right hand, soften the end
of a 'Pyrex' rod in the flame and press it well into the softened end
of the Carius tube.   Continue rotating the work, centre it up,
remove it from the flame, and continue the rotation until the glass
sets.   Then turn off the oxygen delivery valve.   Warm up the
Carius tube about three inches down from the open end, using the
gas–air flame as before.   Subsequently turn on the oxygen.   Hold
the Carius tube in the left hand, the 'Pyrex' rod in the right hand,
keep the work rotating evenly (do not pull) and let the tube soften

and the walls collapse, finally together; then draw off the end, at the same time removing the tube from the flame. This procedure gives a thick-walled seal (see *Figure 51*). Turn off the oxygen (at the main cylinder valve) and the air and turn down the gas. Anneal the glass by rotating the freshly sealed end of the Carius tube in the small yellow flame until it is covered with soot. Allow the tube to cool (out of draughts), wrap the tube in asbestos paper (this is unnecessary if the iron jacket already has an asbestos lining), insert it into the iron jacket and screw on the cap. Heat the tube in the furnace (e.g. Towers' Carius tube furnace) and maintain it at 100° for 4 hours. (On no account remove the Carius tube from the jacket until the pressure has been released.) Allow the tube to cool to *room temperature*, unscrew the cap and slide out the glass Carius tube 2–3 inches only. Clamp the iron jacket to a retort stand in the fume-chamber so that the bottom end of the jacket rests on the tiles and the open end is *ca.* 8 inches above them. *Shield the tube with a safety screen.* Then heat the tip of the Carius tube in a fierce bunsen burner flame. When the glass softens, any excess of pressure in the tube will blow off. Withdraw the Carius tube from the jacket, make a file mark round the end by rotating the tube against the file or glass cutter, hold the tube against the support on the blowpipe, and crack the glass at the file mark with the tip of a 'Pyrex' rod, heated strongly in the oxygen–gas flame.

(c) *Isolation of the product*

Isolate the product without delay because it is sensitive to moisture.

Filter the reaction solution from traces of pigment (phthalocyanine), and evaporate the filtrate, in a 250-c.c. round-bottom flask, to small bulk under reduced pressure (water pump), swirling the flask over the steam-bath (see *Figure 52*). 1 : 3-Di-imino*iso*indoline separates as a faintly green crystalline powder (4–5 g), m.pt 194–195° (decomp.). From methanol–ether (charcoal), it forms colourless prisms. Record the yield and m.pt of the purified product. Bottle and label the specimen.

16

VAPOUR PHASE, CATALYSED REACTIONS

INTRODUCTION

THE reactants are passed as vapour through a hot tube containing a catalyst, and the products are condensed or scrubbed from the issuing gas. Rate of vapour flow, pressure, temperature, and time of contact with the catalyst are readily controllable. Because the method is especially suitable for large scale and continuous operation, it has become increasingly important industrially.

Amongst the many industrial organic chemical processes carried out catalytically in the vapour phase are: cracking of higher crude petroleum fractions to olefines and low molecular weight branched-chain paraffins, and the cracking of natural gas to C_2-C_4 olefines, at 400° over alumina–silica; polymerization of olefines to high octane petroleum at 200°/200 lb/in.^{2} over supported phosphoric acid; dehydrogenation of C_6 and higher paraffins to benzenoid hydrocarbons (e.g. heptane → toluene) at 400° over copper chromite or zinc oxide–alumina; production of methanol from water gas at 200–450°/50–350 atmospheres over zinc chromite; oxidation of ethanol to acetaldehyde with air at 300° over copper gauze; production of acetone from ethanol and steam at 450° over reduced iron oxide–lime.

In the laboratory, there are many preparative applications of the vapour phase catalytic method, e.g. the preparation[1] of aldehydes and ketones by dehydrogenation of primary and secondary alcohols over copper chromite at 320° (see below); the dehydration[2] at 350° of *cyclo*hexanols to *cyclo*hexenes over basic aluminium phosphate; the preparation of dihydropyran from tetrahydrofurfuryl alcohol at 330° over alumina[3]; the cracking of acetates to olefines at 500° over silica[4]; and the preparation of nitriles from carboxylic acids and ammonia at 400° over basic aluminium phosphate[5] (one example is given on p 101). Where applicable, the vapour phase catalytic method is undoubtedly superior to the more conventional laboratory procedures.

REFERENCES

General:

BERKMAN, MORRELL and EGLOFF, *Catalysis*, Reinhold Publishing

Corpn, New York, 1940, Chapter 8 *et seq.*

FRANKENBERG, KOMAREWSKY and RIDEAL, *Advances in Catalysis, and Related Subjects,* Academic Press Inc., New York, 1952, Vol. IV, and previous volumes.

HURD, *The Pyrolysis of Carbon Compounds* (American Chemical Society Monograph No. 50), The Chemical Catalog Company Inc., New York, 1929.

Particular:

[1] ADKINS, KOMMES, STRUSS and DASLER, *J. Amer. chem. Soc.,* 1933, **55**, 2992.

[2] *cf. French Patent No. 679,997* (1928); *British Patent No. 627,453* (1949).

[3] *Org. Synth.,* 1943, **23**, 25.

[4] BURNS, JONES and RITCHIE, *J. chem. Soc.,* **1935**, 400.

[5] *cf. British Patent No. 451,594* (1936); *U.S. Patent No. 2,200,734* (1940).

(i) DEHYDROGENATION OF ALCOHOLS OVER COPPER CHROMITE AT 320°

$$R \cdot CH_2OH \longrightarrow R \cdot CHO + H_2$$

$$RR'CHOH \longrightarrow RR'CO + H_2$$

Catalyst

Dissolve copper nitrate (45 g) in a hot, stirred solution of barium nitrate (5 g) in water (150 c.c.) and to the hot solution add a warm solution of ammonium dichromate (25 g) in a mixture of water (100 c.c.) and concentrated aqueous ammonia (35 c.c.). Stir the mixture for a few minutes and allow it to cool. Collect the precipitate on a 7-cm Buchner filter, wash it with water (200 c.c.), transfer it to a beaker and mix it with sufficient water to form a thin cream. Add pumice (150 g; 3–8 mesh), stir the mixture until the pumice is uniformly coated, and then transfer the mass to a clean iron pan. Stir the mass with a glass rod, and heat it gently to expel the water. Soon, the coated granules of pumice no longer adhere to one another. Continue to stir and heat the mixture until it is uniformly black.

It is unnecessary in the present experiment to pretreat the catalyst with hydrogen, although this increases its efficiency. The operation needs careful control to prevent too extensive reduction of the cupric oxide.

Apparatus

The copper reaction tube (30 × 1 in.) (see *Figure 53*) is heated electrically (rheostat control) by an asbestos-insulated winding capable of giving temperatures up to 450°. The turns of the winding are so spaced that at *ca.* 300°, the temperature is uniform along its length. There is a narrow glass tube down the centre of the reaction tube for a thermocouple junction which is connected to a direct reading indicator (Foster Instrument Co. Ltd, Letchworth, Herts).

Procedure

Push a plug of glass-wool down the copper tube to *f* (*Figure 53*). Insert from the end *d* the thermocouple tube *e* and the 360° thermometer, and work them through the plug at *f*. Invert the copper tube, pour the copper chromite catalyst in (from *h*) and tap the tube gently. Plug the tube at *g* with glass-wool and return the tube to its upright position. Connect the Vigreux column, condenser and receiver *a*, as shown.

Switch on the reaction-tube heater. Clip the tube *c* and draw a *very slow* stream of air through the catalyst by connecting the receiver *a* to a water pump. This process completes the ignition of the catalyst. (Too rapid a stream of air inactivates the catalyst.) When the temperature in the reaction tube at *d* reaches 320°, remove the clip at *c* and disconnect the pump from the receiver *a*. Then attach the boiler *i*, containing the alcohol (any lower primary or secondary carbinol) (100 c.c.) and some porous chips, light the burner beneath the boiler and connect the receiver *a* to the inlet of a Drechsel bottle which contains water. To obtain smooth dehydrogenation of the alcohol, as indicated by a steady and fairly rapid evolution of hydrogen, adjust the heat inputs to the boiler and to the reaction tube, so that:

(*1*) the temperature of the hottest zone in the tube is 320–330° (above 350°, dehydration of the alcohol sets in),

(*2*) the temperature at *b* does not rise above the b.pt of the aldehyde or ketone being formed, and

(*3*) the rate of collection of distillate does not exceed 1 drop/second.

Investigate the temperature along the reaction tube with the movable thermocouple: the reaction is strongly endothermic. Measure the rate of hydrogen evolution by collecting the gas for 5-minute periods: this gives the rate of dehydrogenation.

When the volume of alcohol in the boiler *i* has fallen to *ca.* 20 c.c., disconnect the Drechsel bottle at *a*, remove the burner and switch off the heater. Dry the distillate, which consists of carbonyl compound and a little water, with anhydrous magnesium sulphate,

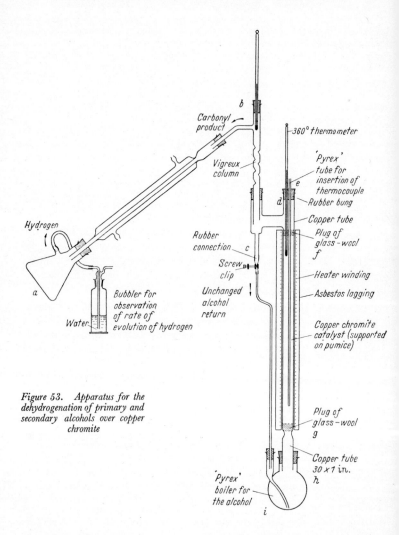

Figure 53. Apparatus for the dehydrogenation of primary and secondary alcohols over copper chromite

and distil the compound slowly through a vacuum-jacketed fractionating column (15 × 1·5 cm) packed with Fenske helices ($\frac{1}{8}$ in.). Weigh the carbonyl compound, calculate the conversion yield (70–90 per cent, depending on the alcohol), and record the boiling point and refractive index. Transfer the sample to a labelled bottle or ampoule.

100

The catalyst becomes deactivated after a period of use. To burn off carbon deposits and reactivate the catalyst, heat it *in situ* to 320° in a *slow* stream of air for *ca.* 1 hour.

(ii) PROPIONITRILE FROM PROPIONIC ACID AND AMMONIA OVER BASIC ALUMINIUM PHOSPHATE AT 400°

(We are indebted to Imperial Chemical Industries Ltd, Billingham Division, Co. Durham, for the experimental details.)

$$Et \cdot CO_2H + NH_3 \longrightarrow Et \cdot CN + 2H_2O$$

A fourfold excess of ammonia is necessary to suppress the formation of diethyl ketone.

Catalyst

Mix a solution of aluminium sulphate [40 g, $Al_2(SO_4)_3 \cdot 18H_2O$] in water (350 c.c.) at *ca.* 30° with a solution containing sodium carbonate (13 g, Na_2CO_3) and disodium hydrogen phosphate (14 g, $Na_2HPO_4 \cdot H_2O$) in water (300 c.c.) at *ca.* 40°. Wash the precipitate several times by decantation with water, make a thin slurry of it in water, and stir in pumice (200 g; 3–8 mesh). Heat the mass on a clean iron tray, and stir the mass with a 500° thermometer (enclosed for protection in a 'Pyrex' glass tube) until the water has evaporated and the temperature in the mass has reached 400° [*cf. British Patent No. 649,980* (1951)].

Apparatus (see Figure 54)

The silica reaction tube (36 × 1 in.) (Thermal Syndicate Ltd, London) is surrounded for a central length of 30 inches by a close-fitting copper tube which carries an electric heater capable of giving temperatures up to 600°: control is by a rheostat. The asbestos-insulated winding covers the middle 24 inches of the copper tube: with this arrangement the temperature along the length of the catalyst is uniform. The temperature of the catalyst is measured with a thermocouple inserted down a narrow, central 'Pyrex' glass tube (20 in. long).

Procedure

Fit the thermocouple tube *f* and the connection to the double surface condenser through the bung at the end *g* of the silica tube, nearest to the indentations at *e*. Push a glass-wool plug from the end *c* down to the indentations. Pour silica chips (20 g; 3/16 in. mesh) into the silica tube (from end *c*) to form a layer above the indentations. Then pour in the basic aluminium phosphate catalyst (170 c.c.) and finally add a 4-in. layer of the silica chips (60 g) to form a preheating zone at *d*. Fit the ammonia inlet

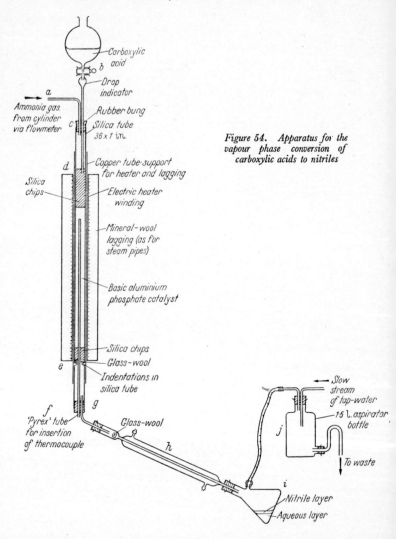

Figure 54. *Apparatus for the vapour phase conversion of carboxylic acids to nitriles*

tube *a* and the 'Pyrex' drop-indicating tap-funnel *b* through the bung at *c*, the holes of which have been smeared with silicone grease, and cautiously work the stem of the funnel about half-an-inch into the layer of silica chips at *d*. Mount the silica tube vertically, as shown, and connect to it the condenser *h* (which has a loose plug of glass-wool at one or both of its ends to aid condensation of mist from the gas stream) and the receiver *i*. Connect the tube *a* via a flowmeter (or a bubbler containing medicinal paraffin) to a cylinder of ammonia, mounted the right way up, and connect the outlet from the receiver *i* to the ammonia-absorption trap *j*. Turn on the water to the trap and to the condenser.

Switch on the reaction-tube heater and adjust the rheostats so as to obtain a uniform temperature of 400–410° along the heated section of the tube. Then, keeping the tube at this temperature, pass ammonia gas (*ca.* 1·7 litre/minute) and add propionic acid (40 c.c.) from the tap-funnel during 30–60 minutes. After a further 5 minutes, turn off the ammonia (at the cylinder) and the water to the trap *j* and then switch off the reaction-tube heater.

Transfer the mixture in the receiver *i* to a 100-c.c. tap-funnel and reject the lower layer (water containing a little ammonium propionate, propionamide, propionitrile and diethyl ketone). Wash the upper layer (propionitrile) twice with an equal volume of a solution of calcium chloride (40 g; anhydrous) in 2N-hydrochloric acid (65 c.c.) and twice with an equal volume of *saturated* sodium carbonate solution. Dry the nitrile with anhydrous calcium chloride and distil the nitrile (b.pt 96–97°) at atmospheric pressure through a vacuum-jacketed fractionating column (15 × 1·5 cm) packed with Fenske helices ($\frac{1}{8}$ in.). Record the yield (*ca.* 80 per cent), boiling point and refractive index of the propionitrile. Transfer the nitrile to a labelled bottle.

The catalyst should remain active for up to 120 hours of use. To burn off carbon deposits and so regenerate the catalyst, heat the catalyst *in situ* at 400° in a slow stream of air (connect a filter-pump to the reaction tube at *g*) for *ca.* 1 hour.

17

REACTION IN LIQUID AMMONIA

INTRODUCTION

LIQUID ammonia is a good solvent for many organic and inorganic substances, including the alkali and alkaline earth metals, and is therefore an excellent medium for certain reactions.

Liquid ammonia is slightly ionized: $2NH_3 \rightleftharpoons NH_4{}^+ + NH_2{}^-$. The ammonium and amide ions are counterparts of the hydroxonium and hydroxyl ions in water: $2H_2O \rightleftharpoons H_3O^+ + OH^-$. Therefore in ammonia, ammonium salts and metal amides function as acids and bases respectively.

Organic reactions which can be carried out in liquid ammonia include: dehydrogenation with sodamide; debenzylation of *O*- and *S*-benzyl ethers and esters with sodium; reduction of acetylenes to (*trans-*) olefines with sodium and, e.g., ethanol; and metallation with sodium or sodamide. In particular, liquid ammonia is an excellent solvent medium for the formation and reactions of sodio-acetylides. The preparative usefulness of acetylenes depends largely on this fact: acetylene itself gives with sodamide in liquid ammonia a *mono*sodio-derivative, whereas with a Grignard reagent it gives a *di*magnesium derivative ($XMg \cdot C \equiv C \cdot MgX$). Sodium acetylide and metallated acetylenes ($R \cdot C \equiv C \cdot M$; $M = Na$, Li, $\frac{1}{2}Ca$, etc.) react, for example, with primary alkyl halides to give alkyl acetylenes and with aldehydes and ketones to form acetylene carbinols.

Acetylene carbinols derived from polyene aldehydes and ketones have been used in Vitamin A and carotenoid syntheses.

REFERENCES

General:

EMELÉUS and ANDERSON, *Modern Aspects of Inorganic Chemistry*, Routledge and Kegan Paul Ltd, London, 1952, Chapter 17.
JOHNSON, *Chem. Rev.*, 1940, **26**, 1.

Reactions of inorganic and organic substances with solutions of metals in liquid ammonia:

Birch, *Quart. Rev. chem. Soc., Lond.*, 1950, **4**, 69.

Fernelius and Watt, *Chem. Rev.*, 1937, **20**, 195.

Watt, *ibid*, 1950, **46**, 289, 317.

Preparation and uses of sodamide in liquid ammonia:

Vaughan, Vogt and Nieuwland, *J. Amer. chem. Soc.*, 1934, **56**, 2120.

Preparation and reactions of acetylene carbinols:

Heilbron, *J. chem. Soc.*, **1948**, 386.

Johnson, *The Chemistry of Acetylenic Compounds*, Edward Arnold and Co., London, 1946, Vol. I.

Oroshnik and Mebane, *J. Amer. chem. Soc.*, 1949, **71**, 2062.

Preparation of Ethynyl Carbinols from Acetylene

The reaction stages are:

$$Na + NH_3 \xrightarrow[(a)\ +H]{Fe} NaNH_2 \xrightarrow[(b)\ +NH_3]{HC\equiv CH} NaC\equiv CH \xrightarrow[(c)]{\underset{R'}{\overset{R}{>}}CO}$$

$$\underset{ONa\ \ (d)}{\underset{R'}{\overset{R}{>}}C\cdot C\equiv CH} \xrightarrow{NH_4Cl} \underset{OH}{\underset{R'}{\overset{R}{>}}C\cdot C\equiv CH} + NaCl + NH_3$$

The operations involving liquid ammonia must be performed in an efficient fume-chamber. Goggles and gloves should be worn, and a respirator fitted with an ammonia-absorbing canister should be at hand.

(a) *Preparation of sodamide in liquid ammonia*
(*cf. Inorg. Synth.*, 1940, **2**, 128.)

Set up the apparatus as in *Figure 55*.

Run liquid ammonia (*ca.* 250 c.c.) from an upturned cylinder into the 500-c.c. three-necked flask which is supported in a bowl of cork chips for thermal insulation. Start the stirrer, and to the liquid ammonia add finely powdered hydrated ferric nitrate (0·1 g) and then sodium (0·1 g). *As soon as* the colour of the liquid changes from blue to brownish-black, add more sodium (11·5 g) (in pieces *ca.* 0·5 cm³) during 10–15 minutes and pass a slow stream

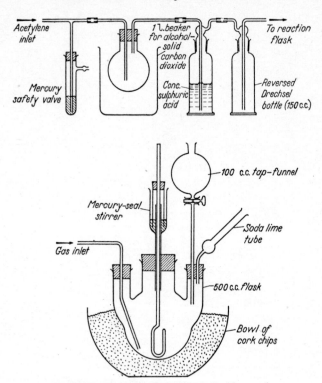

Figure 55. Apparatus for reaction in liquid ammonia

of nitrogen through the liquid ammonia. The colour changes from a deep blue to a light grey after 25–60 minutes when the formation of sodamide is complete. Remove frost on the outside of the flask with alcohol. Add more ammonia, if necessary.

The sodium, dissolved in the liquid ammonia (blue solution), reacts with ammonia in the presence of the iron catalyst to give sodamide (grey suspension) and hydrogen. Sodium peroxide is a promoter, and if there is insufficent oxygen in the liquid ammonia and/or the nitrogen to yield any peroxide, the formation of sodamide occurs only slowly. In that event, bubble air rapidly through the liquid ammonia for a short time.

(b) *Preparation of sodium acetylide*

Connect the acetylene cylinder, through a mercury safety valve, a trap (cooled with solid carbon dioxide and alcohol, to condense out acetone*), a Drechsel bottle containing concentrated sulphuric acid and a reversed empty Drechsel bottle, *in that order* (see *Figure 55*), to the inlet tube of the reaction flask which contains the suspension of sodamide in liquid ammonia. Pass a rapid stream (*ca.* 1 litre/min.) of acetylene until the colour of the reaction mixture darkens (in *ca.* 1 hour). The formation of sodium acetylide is then complete. Add more liquid ammonia, if necessary.

(c) and (d) *Reaction of the sodium acetylide with a carbonyl compound*

Reduce the flow of acetylene to *ca.* 50 c.c./min. and add a solution of the carbonyl compound in dry ether (50 c.c.) during 30 minutes. Use (*i*) *cyclo*hexanone (49 g), or (*ii*) acetone (29 g; dried over potassium carbonate), or (*iii*) benzaldehyde (53 g; freshly distilled). Continue the stirring of the mixture for a further 3 hours and then close the valve on the acetylene cylinder, and remove the gas inlet tube from the reaction flask. Slowly add ammonium chloride (30 g) during 15 minutes. (If necessary, the reaction

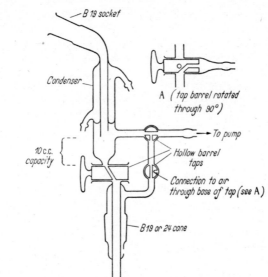

Figure 56. Modified Linstead receiver

mixture can be left overnight at this stage, provided the flask is three quarters filled with liquid ammonia.)

Remove the bowl of cork chips and allow most of the ammonia

---

* The acetylene in the cylinder is in solution in acetone absorbed in a porous solid.

to evaporate. Continue the stirring and hasten the evaporation, if desired, by placing the flask in warm water. Add ether (100 c.c.), filter the mixture and wash the solid on the filter thoroughly with ether (*ca.* 300 c.c.). Distil off *ca.* 200 c.c. of ether from the combined filtrate and washings to expel any ammonia remaining, and shake the residual ether solution with saturated aqueous sodium hydrogen sulphite prepared from sodium metabisulphite (48 g) and water (76 c.c.). Filter the mixture and wash the solid on the filter with ether. Dry the ethereal solution first over anhydrous sodium sulphate and then over anhydrous potassium carbonate, and filter off the drying agent. Run the ethereal solution slowly from a tap-funnel into a 50-c.c. Kon flask heated on the steam-bath, and distil off the ether. Add anhydrous potassium carbonate (0·1 g) to the residual liquid and also put into the flask a boiling-stick or anti-bumping tube (see p 68 and *Figure 36*). Connect the flask to a Perkin triangle or a modified Linstead receiver (see *Figure 56*), and fractionally distil the liquid.

(*i*) *cyclo*Hexanone product. Refractionate the liquid and collect the 1-ethynyl*cyclo*hexanol (12–18 g) at 67–69°/10 mm Hg.

(*ii*) Acetone product. 3-Methylbut-1-yn-3-ol boils at 102–104°/760 mm Hg. [Sometimes the azeotrope, b.pt 90°, with water (26 per cent) is obtained. The water can be removed by anhydrous potassium carbonate.] Yield of carbinol 8–12 g.

(*iii*) Benzaldehyde product. Refractionate the liquid from anhydrous potassium carbonate (0·1 g). The 3-phenylprop-1-yn-3-ol (13–15 g), b.pt 94°/0·7 mm Hg, crystallizes on cooling. Recrystallize the carbinol, m.pt 28·5°, from ether-light petroleum (b.pt 40–60°) at − 40° thus: Place the flask containing the solution in an alcohol-bath and add small pieces of solid carbon dioxide until the temperature (pentane thermometer) has fallen to − 40°. Collect the solid on a cooled filter [see *Figure 29*(b)].

Record the boiling point, refractive index and yield* of the ethynyl carbinol (which should be free from carbonyl compound—test with 2 : 4-dinitrophenylhydrazine reagent). Bottle and label the specimen.

---

* With practice, double the above yields can be obtained.

18

PREPARATIVE USE OF LITHIUM ALUMINIUM HYDRIDE

LITHIUM aluminium hydride is an excellent reagent for the reduction and hydrogenolysis of certain polar groups. For example, -COCl, -CO$_2$H, -CO$_2$Et and -CHO are reduced to -CH$_2$OH, $>$CO to -CHOH, -CONH$_2$ and -CH$=$NOH to -CH$_2$NH$_2$, and primary and secondary alkyl halides are often reduced to hydrocarbons. Carbon–carbon double and triple bonds are unaffected except in some compounds in which they are $\alpha\beta$ to a polar group.

Although the Meerwein–Ponndorf reducing agent is *specific* for carbonyl groups and is therefore to be preferred, e.g. for the reduction of $>$CO in α- or γ-keto-esters, in other cases lithium aluminium hydride has advantages.

Reductions with lithium aluminium hydride proceed at ordinary temperature, or below, and are usually rapid and complete (i.e. free from side reactions). The substance to be reduced is added slowly (sparingly soluble substances by continuous extraction) to an excess of the reagent suspended or dissolved in diethyl ether, tetrahydrofurane or, occasionally, dibutyl ether.

Selective reduction of polar groups in the presence of other reducible functions can frequently be achieved by an inverse addition method: the reagent is added slowly to the substance to be reduced so that the reagent is never present in excess. Thus by inverse addition -CN can be reduced to -CH$=$NH (normal addition gives -CH$_2$NH$_2$) and cinnamaldehyde, for example, to cinnamyl alcohol (normal addition gives hydrocinnamyl alcohol).

REFERENCES

ADAMS, *Organic Reactions*, John Wiley and Sons, Inc., New York, 1951, Vol. VI, Chapter 10.

For the related reagents, lithium and sodium borohydrides, see:
CHAIKIN and BROWN, *J. Amer. chem. Soc.*, 1949, **71**, 122.
NYSTROM, CHAIKIN and BROWN, *ibid*, p 3245.

NOTE

Because of hydrogen evolution, remove all flames etc. from the vicinity of the apparatus. Use a shielded or brushless stirrer motor.

(i) REDUCTION OF CINNAMALDEHYDE TO HYDROCINNAMYL ALCOHOL

Normal addition

(*cf.* NYSTROM and BROWN, *J. Amer. chem. Soc.*, 1947, **69**, 1197, 2548; 1948, **70**, 3738.)

Dry in an oven, a 500-c.c. three-necked flask, a 100-c.c. tap-funnel and a double-surface condenser.

Powder, in a mortar, lumps of lithium aluminium hydride (2·9 g; 0·076 mole; 33 per cent excess) *under* diethyl ether (dried over sodium) and wash the slurry into the three-necked flask with dry ether (total 100 c.c.). Set up the apparatus as shown in *Figure 57* and switch on the stirrer. From the dropping funnel

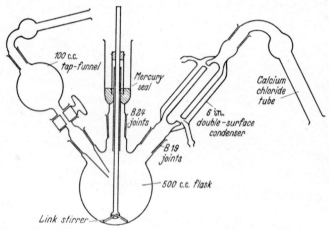

Figure 57. *Apparatus for reductions with lithium aluminium hydride:* (i) *normal addition*

add a solution of cinnamaldehyde (redistilled; 10 g; 0·076 mole) in dry ether (75 c.c.) at such a rate that the ether in the flask refluxes gently. Ten minutes after completion of the addition, cool the flask in water and ice, and *cautiously* add water (12 c.c.) to the stirred reaction mixture to decompose the excess of the reagent. Then add 10 per cent sulphuric acid (95 c.c.). Separate the ether layer and extract the aqueous layer with ether (2 × 30 c.c.). Dry the combined ether solutions over anhydrous sodium sulphate, and by distillation, eventually under reduced pressure, isolate the hydrocinnamyl alcohol (b.pt 120–121°/13 mm Hg;

8–9 g). Test the product with 2 : 4-dinitrophenylhydrazine reagent to confirm the absence of cinnamaldehyde.

Record the boiling point, refractive index and yield of the alcohol, and transfer the sample to a labelled bottle or ampoule.

(ii) REDUCTION OF CINNAMALDEHYDE TO CINNAMYL ALCOHOL

Inverse addition

(*cf.* HOCHSTEIN and BROWN, *J. Amer. chem. Soc.*, 1948, **70**, 3484.)

Make up and filter a solution of lithium aluminium hydride (*ca.* 1 g) in dry diethyl ether (50 c.c.) in the manner described on p 143.

Determine the reagent content of the solution: Dilute a 2·0-c.c. portion with dry ether to 25·0 c.c. in a standard flask, mix the solution, and, with the Zerewitinoff apparatus (*Figure 71*), measure the hydrogen evolved on treatment of 5·0-c.c. portions with water (5 c.c.);

$$LiAlH_4 + 4H_2O \rightarrow LiOH + Al(OH)_3 + 4H_2$$

From the observations, calculate the lithium aluminium hydride content of the original reagent solution in g/c.c.

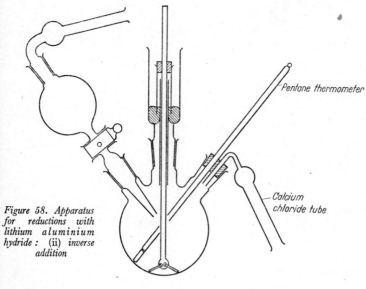

Figure 58. *Apparatus for reductions with lithium aluminium hydride :* (ii) *inverse addition*

Pentane thermometer

Calcium chloride tube

Set up the dried apparatus, as in *Figure 58*, with a solution of cinnamaldehyde (redistilled; 10 g; 0·076 mole) in dry ether (25 c.c.) in the flask. Switch on the stirrer, cool the flask with an ice–salt-bath until the internal temperature reaches $- 10°$ (pentane or alcohol thermometer), and add a 10 per cent excess of the lithium aluminium hydride (0·78 g) in ether during *ca.* 30 minutes so that the temperature remains below $+ 10°$. Add water (3 c.c.) cautiously to the stirred reaction mixture to decompose the excess of the reagent and then add 10 per cent sulphuric acid (25 c.c.). Separate the ether layer and extract the aqueous layer with ether (2×50 c.c.). Dry the combined ether layers over sodium sulphate. Evaporate the ether, and, by distilling the residue under reduced pressure, isolate the cinnamyl alcohol (b.pt 139°/14 mm Hg; 8–9 g): it will crystallize when cooled (m.pt 33°).

Record the melting point, boiling point and yield of the cinnamyl alcohol, and bottle the specimen.

19

PREPARATIVE ELECTROLYSIS

INTRODUCTION

THERE are three main types of preparative electrolysis, (a) cathodic reduction, (b) anodic oxidation and (c) anodic coupling.

Anodic coupling was first described by KOLBE[1] who electrolysed salts of aliphatic carboxylic acids, $R \cdot CO_2H$, and obtained various products including carbon dioxide and hydrocarbons, $R \cdot R$;

$$2R \cdot CO_2{}^- \rightarrow R \cdot R + 2CO_2 + 2e$$

Electrolyses of this type afford convenient synthetic routes to many compounds of symmetrical structure, e.g. perhydrobixin and perhydrocrocetin[2]. Good yields are generally obtained with aliphatic carboxylic acids and half-esters of dicarboxylic acids, which are unsubstituted in the position α to the carboxyl group. Only small yields of coupled product have been reported from $\alpha\beta$- and $\beta\gamma$-unsaturated acids and from benzoic acid.

The Kolbe reaction is not restricted to the synthesis of compounds with symmetrical structures. Electrolysis of mixtures of carboxylic acids or half esters, $R \cdot CO_2H$ and $R' \cdot CO_2H$, gives the products $R \cdot R$, $R' \cdot R'$ and $R \cdot R'$. By adjustment of the proportions of the starting materials, the unsymmetrical product $R \cdot R'$ can be obtained in good yield (e.g. as in the synthesis of $\pm$ muscone[3]).

The solvent for anodic coupling reactions is usually water or methanol. In water, optimum yields are obtained with a high concentration of the carboxylic acid containing a small proportion of the sodium salt, a temperature below 5°, a smooth platinum anode and a high current density. With these conditions, side reactions leading to the formation of alcohols (Hofer–Moest reaction) and olefines are minimized. In methanol, the conditions for optimum yields appear to be less critical.

REFERENCES

General:

BROCKMAN, *Electro-organic Chemistry*, John Wiley and Sons Inc., New York, 1926.

113

SWANN, *Trans. electrochem. Soc.*, 1936, **69**, 287; 1940, **77**, 460; 1945, **88**, 104.

WEEDON, *Quart. Rev. chem. Soc., Lond.*, 1952, **6**, 380.

WEISSBERGER, *Technique of Organic Chemistry*, Interscience Publishers, Inc., New York, 1948, Vol. II, p 143 *et seq.*

Particular:

[1] KOLBE, *Liebigs Ann.*, 1849, **69**, 257.

[2] KARRER, BENZ, MORF, RAUDNITZ, STOLL and TAKAHASHI, *Helv. chim. Acta*, 1932, **15**, 1399; KARRER, BENZ and STOLL, *ibid*, 1933, **16**, 297.

[3] HUNSDIECKER, *Ber. dtsch. chem. Ges.*, 1942, **75**, 1197.

PREPARATION OF HEXACOSANE

Dissolve myristic acid (purified; 5·0 g) in a warm solution of sodium methoxide (from 0·1 g of sodium) in methanol (25 c.c.) contained in a cylindrical cell (25 × 3 cm). At once insert the platinum plate electrodes (3 × 2 cm; gap 4–8 mm) (see *Figure 59*). Connect the electrodes to a d.c. supply (120 volts) through

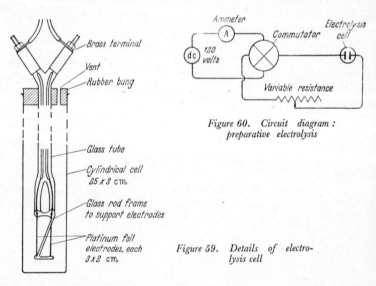

Figure 60. *Circuit diagram: preparative electrolysis*

Figure 59. *Details of electrolysis cell*

a variable resistance, an ammeter and a commutator (see *Figure 60*) and pass a current of *ca.* 1 amp. If the current falls because of coating of the electrodes with insoluble by-products, reverse its

114

direction from time to time with the commutator switch. During the electrolysis cool the cell in a bath of cold water containing ice.

When the electrolyte becomes weakly alkaline (pH 7–8, wide-range indicator paper) switch off the current. Neutralize the cell contents with acetic acid (a few drops) and then evaporate most of the solvent under reduced pressure (apparatus, *Figure 52*). Pour the residue into water and extract the mixture with ether. Wash the ethereal solution with dilute sodium hydroxide* and with water, dry the solution over calcium chloride and evaporate the ether. Crystallize the residue from light petroleum (b.pt 40–60°). Record the yield (2·0–2·4 g) and melting point of the hexacosane (m.pt 57–58°) and bottle and label the specimen.

---

* If the electrolysis has not been carried to completion, trouble is encountered at this stage. If sodium myristate separates, filter it off. If the two phases emulsify, dissolve sodium hydroxide in the mixture, cool, and add more ether and water.

20

OZONOLYSIS

INTRODUCTION

OZONE readily attacks ethylenic linkages (one molecule reacts/ double bond), and from the products carbonyl compounds can be obtained. The process results in separation of the carbon atoms originally united by double bonds. The identities and yields of carbonyl products provide information on the positions of the double bonds in the olefine. Hence ozonolysis is frequently used in structure elucidation.

STAUDINGER[1] suggested that the first product was the ozonide (*I*) which then changed (sometimes explosively) into an *iso*ozonide (*II*) (or to a polymer).

$$(I) \qquad\qquad (II)$$

Recent work by CRIEGEE[2] indicates that ozone can split double bonds directly with formation of $>CO$ and peroxidic products such as

where HX is the solvent. Attack by ozone on aromatic systems may occur via a π-complex[3].

When the ozonization product is treated with water, or is reduced, two carbonyl functions are formed per original double bond. In the reaction with water, carboxylic acids may be obtained instead of aldehydes which would be given by the reduction method. Treatment of the ozonization product with peracids affords ketones and carboxylic acids directly[4].

A stream of dry ozonized oxygen (1–15 per cent ozone) from a high-tension discharge apparatus is passed through a solution of the olefine in a solvent inert to ozone, such as acetic acid, carbon tetrachloride, chloroform, hexane or ethyl acetate, at or below room temperature until ozone is no longer rapidly absorbed. Over-ozonization leads to general oxidative decomposition and must be avoided.

The ozonization product is then treated in one of the ways already indicated. There is, of course, a variety of methods for isolating the scission products.

REFERENCES

LONG, *Chem. Rev.*, 1940, **27**, 437.

[1] STAUDINGER, *Ber. dtsch. chem. Ges.*, 1925, **58**, 1088.

[2] CRIEGEE, *Liebigs Ann.*, 1953, **583**, 1; BLUNT and LOHAUS, *ibid*, p 2; LOHAUS, *ibid*, p 6.

[3] BADGER, *Rec. Trav. chim. Pays-Bas*, 1952, **71**, 468.

[4] WILMS, *Liebigs Ann.*, 1950, **567**, 96.

NOTE

Most ozonides are explosive. It is advisable to wear goggles and to shield the apparatus with armoured-glass screens.

(i) OZONOLYSIS OF 2 : 4 : 4-TRIMETHYL-1-PENTENE

$$Me_3C \cdot CH_2 \cdot CMe = CH_2 \rightarrow Me_3C \cdot CH_2 \cdot COMe + CH_2O$$

Formaldehyde is isolated as its dimedone derivative and then methyl neopentyl ketone as its 2 : 4-dinitrophenylhydrazone.

Turn on a slow stream of oxygen (via a diaphragm reducing valve; type BOR 12, British Oxygen Co. Ltd) to the ozone generator and, after 2–3 minutes, switch on the electricity supply to the generator (J. W. Towers and Co. Ltd).

Weigh to the nearest milligramme *ca.* 800 mg of the olefine (pure; British Petroleum Co., Sunbury-on-Thames, Middlesex) into a test-tube ($2 \times \frac{1}{2}$ in.) supported in a partially bored cork. Place glacial acetic acid (50 c.c.) in the reaction bottle (a 150-c.c. Drechsel bottle) and carefully add the tube containing the olefine. Replace the gas inlet tube and mix the contents of the bottle. Immerse the reaction bottle, almost to the neck, in cold water in a 1-litre beaker. Connect the inlet tube to the ozone generator with PVC tubing and the outlet tube to a trap (a 150-c.c. Drechsel

bottle) containing distilled water (50 c.c.) (see *Figure 61*). Connect
the outlet tube from the trap to tubing which leads outside the
laboratory (or alternatively, to a tower filled with broken glass
which has been moistened with concentrated aqueous sodium
hydroxide): ozone is unpleasant and is a lung irritant. Adjust
the gas stream to yield *ca.* 0·01 mole of ozone/1·5 hours. It is
convenient to have this rate expressed as flowmeter reading or
bubbles/second (see note on calibration, below).

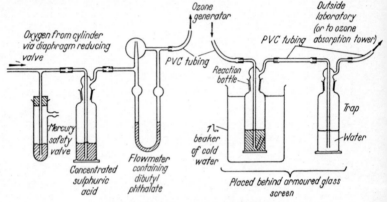

Figure 61. Apparatus for ozonization

After about 80 minutes, test the exit gases from the trap (second
Drechsel bottle) for ozone with moist starch–iodide paper. When
uptake of ozone is complete (shown by its appearance in the exit
gases), disconnect the Drechsel bottles, and connect the ozone
generator to the tube which leads outside the laboratory (or to the
absorption tower). Pour the contents of the reaction bottle into
a 250-c.c. steam distillation flask, containing zinc dust (2 g).
Rinse the bottle with the water in the trap, and add the rinsings
to the flask. Set up the apparatus as in *Figure 62* and steam
distil the mixture as rapidly as is consistent with the distillate
coming over cold. Do not heat the flask. Continue passing steam
until the carbonyl compounds have come over (*ca.* 250 c.c. of
distillate)—test the fresh distillate at intervals with 2 : 4-dinitro-
phenylhydrazine reagent (see below).

Cool the steam distillate in ice-water, add 4 drops of phenolphthalein solution and neutralize the distillate with 40 per cent
sodium hydroxide (*ca.* 70 c.c.). If the solution becomes permanently pink, make it just acid with acetic acid. Add a solution

of dimedone (5 : 5-dimethyl-1 : 3-*cyclo*hexanedione) (3·0 g) in
50 per cent aqueous ethanol (50 c.c.). After 30–60 minutes
collect the precipitate, wash it with 20 per cent aqueous ethanol
(10 c.c.), recrystallize it, if necessary, from ethanol–water and
dry it in a vacuum desiccator over calcium chloride. Record the
melting point and the weight (*ca.* 1 g) of the formaldehyde dimedone.
Transfer the derivative to a labelled specimen tube.

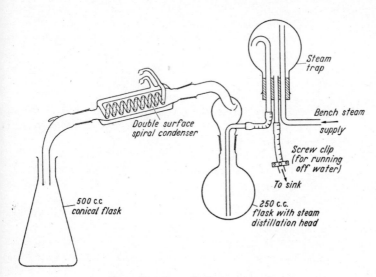

Figure 62.   Steam distillation apparatus

From a 1-litre flask, steam distil the filtrate from the dimedone
derivative until the ketone has all come over—test the fresh distillate
at intervals with 2 : 4-dinitrophenylhydrazine reagent. Add the
distillate (*ca.* 30 c.c.) to a warm solution of 2 : 4-dinitrophenyl-
hydrazine, prepared by dissolving the reagent (2 g) in concentrated
sulphuric acid (20 c.c.) and adding ethanol (50 c.c.). After 30–60
minutes, filter off the derivative, wash it with two 10-c.c. portions
of 30 per cent aqueous ethanol, recrystallize it, if necessary, from
methanol, and dry it in a vacuum desiccator. Record the melting
point and weight (*ca.* 1 g) of the methyl neopentyl ketone 2 : 4-
dinitrophenylhydrazone.

Express the yields of the scission products in mols./mol. of
olefine.

I   119

(ii) Ozonolysis of an Isomeric Olefine
(e.g. Me₃C·CH=CMe₂)

The mixture of carbonyl scission products is reacted with 2 : 4-dinitrophenyl-hydrazine, and the derivatives are separated by chromatography.

Whilst the first steam distillation in the previous experiment is in progress, weigh the olefine (*ca.* 400 mg) into a small test-tube, place the tube in the reaction bottle with acetic acid (25 c.c.) and crush the tube with a glass rod. Put water (25 c.c.) in the trap. Ozonize the olefine solution as before. After 45 minutes, test the exit gases for ozone, and, when a strongly positive test is obtained, disconnect the bottles and steam distil their contents from a 250-c.c. flask in the presence of zinc dust (1 g) (do not heat the flask) until the carbonyl products have distilled over (*ca.* 350 c.c. of distillate).

Meanwhile, connect the ozone generator to the tube leading outside the laboratory and switch off the electricity supply. When the ozone has been swept out of the generator, i.e. after *ca.* 10 minutes, turn off the oxygen cylinder at the main valve.

Pour the steam distillate into 2 : 4-dinitrophenylhydrazine solution, prepared as before from 2 g of the reagent. After 30–60 minutes, collect the precipitate, wash it with water, and dry it in a vacuum desiccator.

Chromatograph a 200-mg portion of the mixed 2 : 4-dinitrophenylhydrazones in chloroform (20 c.c.) on a column (12 × 1·8 cm) of a mixture of kieselguhr ('acid-washed') (4 g) and bentonite (16 g), packed as a thick slurry in chloroform (see p 5). Develop the column with chloroform. Unchanged reagent remains at the top as a red band and the derivatives separate as a fast-moving yellow band and a slow-moving orange band. When the material of the yellow band has passed into the eluate, wash the orange band down the column with 1/1 chloroform–ethanol, and collect the eluate separately. Evaporate the solutions, and determine the yields and melting points of the two derivatives, and thence calculate the yields of the carbonyl scission products. Indicate that the results confirm the structure of the olefine.

2 : 4-Dinitrophenylhydrazones	M.pt (literature)
Acetone	128°
Formaldehyde	155° 168° (2 forms)
Methyl neopentyl ketone	101–102°
Pivalic aldehyde	210°

CALIBRATION OF THE OZONE GENERATOR

Pass the gas from the ozone generator through 50 c.c. of a 5 per cent solution of potassium iodide in 1/1 acetic acid–water contained in the reaction bottle and then through water (50 c.c.) in the trap. After 90 minutes, pour the contents of the reaction bottle into a 250-c.c. conical flask, rinsing the reaction bottle with the contents of the trap;

$$O_3 + 2I^- + 2H^+ \rightarrow H_2O + 2I + O_2$$

Titrate the liberated iodine with 0·1N-sodium thiosulphate.

The output of ozone in moles/hour is with respect to the set rate of gas flow (flowmeter reading or bubbles/second).

PART III

TECHNIQUES OF QUANTITATIVE ANALYSIS AND ALLIED PHYSICAL MEASUREMENTS

NOTES ON THE WEIGHING OF SMALL
QUANTITIES OF SOLIDS
AND LIQUIDS

THE semi-micro balance (e.g. Model M.C.1.A., Stanton Instruments Ltd, London) is 10–100 times more sensitive than an ordinary analytical balance, and is capable of weighing objects accurately to 0·01 mg. Its correct use demands extra precautions. Use the balance with great care and do not attempt to make adjustments.

Load and unload the pans through the *side* windows as far as possible, and keep the front window closed to prevent the breath entering the case. Shut the windows gently. Never release the balance beam when the case is open.

Do not put more than twenty grammes weight on each pan. Operate the rider weights with care; raise and lower the balance beam smoothly.

Keep the balance scrupulously clean. Put the plastic cover over the case when the weighings have been completed.

Do not touch weights or glassware (e.g. weighing bottles) with the fingers: use forceps or tongs, or small chamois leather squares to protect the glassware from the fingers. Carefully wipe, with a chamois leather, glassware which has been handled. In any event keep all objects, which are to be weighed, in or beside the balance for at least 10 minutes, so that they reach temperature and moisture equilibrium with the atmosphere: it is best not to have a desiccant in the balance case. Objects such as specimen tubes which carry paper labels or cellophane-covered corks do not come to a constant weight and cannot therefore be weighed accurately to 0·01 mg until the label or cork has been removed. Keep the balance weights (10 g, downwards), the counterpoises and the forceps permanently in the balance case.

When an object has to be weighed frequently, use a counterpoise to save time. Adjust the counterpoise, e.g. a piece of copper wire, or a 2-c.c. flask containing lead shot, to weigh a fraction of 1 mg less than the object.

When there is an interval of more than a few minutes between consecutive weighings of an object, zero the balance before each

125

weighing, i.e. release the unladen beam and adjust the hairline to coincide with the zero mark on the illuminated scale image before making the weighing.

Always weigh small quantities of solids or liquids in small, very light containers: the balance pan is too small to accommodate even a 10-c.c. standard flask, for example. *Use the following procedures and devices.*

A stable solid—Weigh it (*a*) *into* a boat, weighing-pot or -bucket, or (*b*) if such a container is not required subsequently, *from* a weighing-stick (see *Figure 63*).

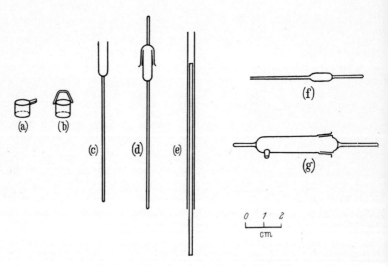

Figure 63. Devices for the weighing of small quantities of solids and liquids : (a) *weighing-pot,* (b) *weighing-bucket* [(a) *and* (b) *constructed from* 2 × ⅜ *in. specimen-tubes*], (c) *weighing-stick,* (d) *capped weighing-stick,* (e) *plunger-type weighing-stick,* (f) *ampoule for liquids (unsealed),* (g) *weighing-pig*

(*a*) Add the solid with a micro-spatula to the tared boat, weighing-pot or -bucket, placed on a piece of clean glass *outside* the balance case. Dust the sides of the weighing device with a fine camel-hair brush before returning the device with contents to the balance pan for reweighing.

(*b*) Push the container end of the weighing-stick into the solid substance (hold the handle with a leather), or introduce the solid with a micro-spatula, dust the outside with a fine brush, and hang the stick (with contents) horizontally on the balance hooks and weigh the stick. Then insert the stick into e.g. a standard flask, and tap out most of the contents. Then reweigh the stick. For a solid which sticks to glass, use the plunger-type weighing-stick [*Figure 63*(e)].

A volatile, deliquescent or unstable solid—Weigh it *in* a boat contained in a pig or weigh it *in* a capped weighing-stick [see *Figure 63*].

A stable, non-volatile liquid—Weigh it *into* a boat, weighing-pot or -bucket. Add the liquid to the tared device, *outside* the balance case, with a fine dropper. Then return the device to the balance pan for the reweighing. If the liquid is required in a standard flask, for example, rinse the liquid with a solvent from the weighing-pot into the flask, via a funnel.

A volatile, or sensitive liquid—Weigh it *in* an ampoule [see *Figure 63*(f)] made from thin glass tube (2–3 mm internal diameter). Clean chemically and dry a 10-cm length of the glass tubing. Make a thick seal about 4 cm from one end, in a small hot flame, and draw off a solid handle 2–3 cm long. Then draw off the other end of the tube to a fine capillary, *ca.* 1 cm from the base of the handle. Cut the capillary so that it is *ca.* 3 cm long. Wipe the ampoule with a leather, and, after 10 minutes, weigh the ampoule. Introduce the liquid into the ampoule by suction (apparatus, *Figure 76*), centrifuge the liquid down to the closed end (hand centrifuge, *Figure 40*), cool the ampoule (held by the capillary end) in ice-water and seal the tip of the ampoule in a small hot flame. Wipe the ampoule with a leather, and, after 10 minutes, reweigh the ampoule (with contents). Make a scratch near the base of the capillary with the sharp edge of a piece of broken tile and break the ampoule at the last possible moment as it is being introduced into e.g. a flask, combustion tube, etc.

21

SEMI-MICRO DETERMINATION OF CARBON AND HYDROGEN

QUANTITATIVE determination of the elements in organic compounds is fundamentally important at all stages of organic chemical research, for checking the identity of substances and for calculating the empirical formulae of new compounds. The most important determination is that of carbon and hydrogen by combustion. There are numerous variations in the details of the method.

In the method described below, the compound is heated in a controlled stream of oxygen and the vapours are passed through copper oxide at 600° to complete the combustion. The gaseous combustion products are carbon dioxide and water, together with sulphur trioxide and sometimes the dioxide (if the compound contained sulphur), nitrogen and oxides of nitrogen (from nitrogenous compounds) and chlorine, bromine or iodine (if the compound contained these elements). The gases are passed through sintered precipitated silver to remove halogens and some of the sulphur trioxide, and through lead peroxide (heated by a decalin boiler) to remove the nitrogen oxides and the last traces of sulphur oxides.

Silver wire, in the constricted end of the combustion tube to which the absorption train is attached, conducts heat which prevents condensation of water from the gases before they pass into the absorption tubes. The water is absorbed in a weighed tube containing anhydrone, and the carbon dioxide in a weighed tube packed with soda–asbestos. The percentage of carbon and of hydrogen in the substance is then calculated from the weights of the carbon dioxide and of the water collected.

REFERENCES

GRANT, *Pregl's Quantitative Organic Microanalysis*, J. and A. Churchill Ltd, London, 1951, Chapter 3.

MILTON and WATERS, *Methods of Quantitative Micro-analysis*, Part 2. Edward Arnold (Publishers) Ltd, London, 1949.

NIEDERL and NIEDERL, *Micromethods of Quantitative Organic Elementary Analysis*, John Wiley and Sons, Inc., New York, 1938, Chapter 5.

STEYERMARK, *Quantitative Organic Microanalysis*, The Blakiston Co., New York, 1951.

DETERMINATION OF CARBON AND HYDROGEN
(apparatus, *Figure 64*)

Switch on the main combustion furnace *e* and the decalin boiler *f*. Check that the combustion tube is stoppered at *g*. Pass a slow stream of oxygen to the flowmeter *a* (taps *1* and *2* open) for 30 minutes. (Use a diaphragm reducing valve on the oxygen cylinder, *cf.* p 117.)

Remove the stopper on the combustion tube at *g* and put on a rubber connector (impregnated with paraffin wax), remove the rubber caps on the absorption tubes and connect the tubes to the apparatus as shown (*Figure 65*). All the details are important: each tube and each connector *must* be the correct way round and in the correct position, as shown. Handle the tubes with pieces of leather (e.g. 3·5 in.²); only the rubber connectors and caps may be touched with the fingers. Keep the leathers and rubber stoppers, connectors and caps in a covered dish when not in use. Test the apparatus for leaks: open the tap on the Mariotte bottle *i* and close tap *2* of the flowmeter—the flow of water should cease.

Re-open tap *2* of the flowmeter *a*. Adjust the rate of oxygen-flow through the apparatus to 7–8 c.c./minute by altering the angle of the outflow tube from the Mariotte bottle *i*. Also adjust tap *1* of the flowmeter to give a reading of 2–3 cm of dibutyl phthalate on the manometer. Continue to pass oxygen through the apparatus, until 30 c.c. of water have been collected. Close the tap of the Mariotte bottle *i*, and disconnect the absorption tubes, again handling the glass with the leathers. Stopper the open end *g* of the combustion tube. Place the rubber connectors in the covered glass dish. Wipe the absorption tubes with the leathers and leave the tubes in a wire rack for 10 minutes beside the balance. (Do not replace the rubber end-pieces.) Empty the measuring cylinder.

Meanwhile weigh the boat on the micro-balance (see p 125). Use the forceps to lift the boat from the polished brass stand under the glass cover (see *Figure 64*) to the balance pan. (All the weights required for the determination are kept inside the balance case.) Then with the forceps lift the boat from the balance pan on to the glass cover (outside the balance case) and with a micro-spatula

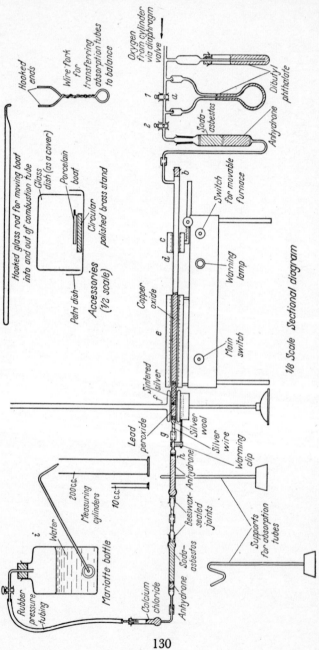

Figure 64. Apparatus for determination of carbon and hydrogen

130

introduce not less than 10 mg and not more than 12 mg of substance. Dust the sides of the boat with a camel-hair brush and
reweigh the boat. Return the boat to the brass stand (using the
forceps) and replace the glass cover.

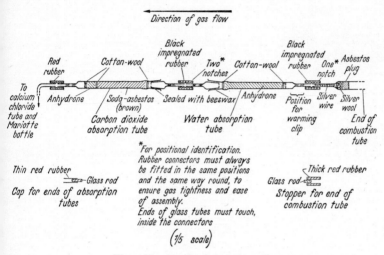

Figure 65. Details of absorption train

At the tenth minute after disconnecting the absorption tubes,
zero the balance. Transfer the carbon dioxide absorption tube
(with the brown filling) from the wire rack on to the balance
hooks: hold the tube with the metal fork or with a leather. Place
the absorption tube so that the balance pan hangs straight. Weigh
the absorption tube to 0·01 mg (see p 125). Then weigh the
water absorption tube. Replace the weights in the balance case
after use.

Commence the combustion *within 30 minutes* of the weighing of
the water absorption tube.

Remove the stopper from the combustion tube at *g* and connect
up the absorption tubes in *exactly* the same manner as before.
Slip the warming clip *h* over the end of the water absorption tube.
Remove the rubber bung *b* and with the forceps introduce the
boat into the combustion tube. With a blunt-ended glass rod,
push the boat just beyond the movable furnace *c* to position *d*.
Replace the rubber bung *b*. Open the tap of the Mariotte bottle *i*,
and switch on the movable furnace *c*.

After several minutes, move the furnace c forward gradually. The substance melts and vaporizes and may char. Move the furnace very slowly so as to keep the reading on the flowmeter constant. During the combustion and the absorption of the combustion products, the outflow from the Mariotte bottle ceases (at *ca.* 90–100 c.c. outflow). When this occurs, stop moving the furnace forwards and, if necessary, move it back a little to keep the flowmeter reading constant. After two or three minutes gradually move the furnace c forwards again, finally right up to the combustion furnace, and leave it there whilst 10 c.c. of water are collected from i. Then move the furnace c right back to the starting position and advance it gradually to the combustion furnace during the next 50–60 c.c. of gas flow. Then switch off the small furnace.

When a total of 200 c.c. of gas has passed, turn off the tap of the Mariotte bottle i. Disconnect the absorption tubes, holding the tubes with the leathers, and remove the rubber connectors. Place the connectors in the covered dish. Wipe the tubes with the leathers, and place the tubes (not stoppered) in the wire rack beside the balance case. Stopper the end g of the combustion tube. After 10 minutes zero the balance and weigh the tubes, the carbon dioxide absorption tube first.

Meanwhile remove the stopper b from the combustion tube and withdraw the combustion boat to the end of the combustion tube with a hooked glass rod. With the forceps, remove the boat from the tube and place it on the brass stand, to cool, under the glass cover. Replace the stopper b.

When the absorption tubes have been weighed, weigh a second sample into the boat as before and repeat the combustion and weighings.

Finally switch off the main furnace and the decalin boiler, close the main valve of the oxygen cylinder and close tap *2* of the flowmeter. Put the rubber caps on the absorption tubes and make sure that the combustion tube has been stoppered.

Give the results of each analysis in the form: Found: C,   ; H,   %. The factors are: C in CO_2, (log) $\bar{1}$·4359; H in H_2O, (log) $\bar{1}$·0488. The results should agree to within 0·3 of a unit for both C and H.

NOTES

PACKING OF THE ABSORPTION TUBES (see *Figure 65*)

(a) *Water absorption tube*

Warm the stoppered end of the tube *very gently* by rotating it near a small bunsen burner flame.   The absorption tubes are made from soda glass and will crack if placed *in* a flame.   When the wax has softened, remove the stopper.   Clean the stopper and socket with benzene-moistened cotton-wool.   Empty the absorption tube, clean it if necessary with hydrochloric acid, wash the tube with distilled water and dry it in the oven.   Push a plug of cotton-wool (3–4 mm) to the end of the absorption tube.   Fill the tube to within 5 mm of the ground-glass socket with micro-analytical reagent grade anhydrone (14–22 mesh) and then add a plug of cotton-wool.   Warm the stopper carefully near a small bunsen burner flame and apply a little beeswax to the surface of the stopper. Immediately insert the stopper in the socket of the absorption tube.   A transparent seal should be obtained.   Remove any excess of beeswax from the rim of the joint with benzene-moistened cotton-wool.   If the tube is not to be used at once, fit it with rubber caps.

(b) *Carbon dioxide absorption tube*

Clean and dry the tube in the manner described above.   Introduce a cotton-wool plug, a 2–3 cm layer of anhydrone (to prevent loss of moisture which might be driven out of the soda–asbestos), a cotton-wool plug, micro-analytical reagent grade soda–asbestos (14–22 mesh) and another cotton-wool plug, in that order.   Stopper the tube as described above.

PACKING OF THE COMBUSTION TUBE

If the combustion tube is new, clean it with chromic–sulphuric acid, wash it with distilled water and dry it.   Clean a used combustion tube with a twist of cotton-wool (moistened with 40 per cent hydrofluoric acid) on the end of a copper rod.   Wash the tube with distilled water and dry it.

Push silver-wool down the tube to form a layer 2 mm thick at the constricted end and follow it with a plug (*ca.* 5 mm thick) of freshly ignited asbestos-wool.   This plug cuts down the rate of gas flow through the tube.   Tamp down the asbestos with the copper rod.   Connect the combustion tube to the Mariotte bottle and observe the rate of outflow. Adjust the amount of asbestos-wool so that the outflow is 15 c.c./minute.

Make a paste of brown 'AnalaR' lead peroxide and water, dry it on a clock-glass and break up the solid into small pieces (*ca.* 2 mm³) with a spatula. Introduce a 4-cm layer of the lead peroxide pieces into the combustion tube and tap the tube gently so that the peroxide packs down. Then push in a plug (2 mm thick) of freshly ignited asbestos-wool. Clean all traces of lead peroxide from the unpacked section of the combustion tube with cotton-wool on the end of the copper rod.

Dissolve silver nitrate (10 g) in the minimum of water, add small pieces of pure copper foil (4 g), and, when most of the copper has dissolved (several hours), wash the crystalline silver on a filter with 1 per cent hydrochloric acid. Pick out any pieces of copper. Heat the silver gently in a porcelain evaporating dish over a small bunsen burner flame until it sinters to a spongy mass. Break up the cooled mass with a spatula. Place a 4-cm layer of the sintered silver in the combustion tube and follow it with a 2-mm thick plug of freshly ignited asbestos-wool.

Introduce micro-analytical reagent grade copper oxide ('from wire'), freshly ignited at about 600°, into the combustion tube to a length 1·5 cm less than that of the combustion furnace, i.e. so that there is *ca.* 18 cm of copper oxide. The main furnace will then surround the copper oxide filling and about one third of the sintered silver. Push in a final plug of freshly ignited asbestos.

Push silver wire (*ca.* 2·5 cm long) into the constricted end of the combustion tube so that it contacts the layer of silver-wool.

Push the combustion tube into the furnace to the position shown in *Figure 64*. Connect the flowmeter, switch on the main furnace and the decalin boiler and pass oxygen through the combustion tube at 7–8 c.c./minute for at least 10 hours. Then perform 4–6 combustions of 'AnalaR' benzoic acid. Normally, the results from only the first 2–3 combustions are inaccurate. The tube is then ready for use. Keep the prepared combustion tube stoppered when not in use.

22

MICRO KJELDAHL DETERMINATION OF NITROGEN

Introduction

THE organic nitrogenous compound is digested with concentrated sulphuric acid in the presence of selenium and copper sulphate–potassium sulphate catalysts to yield ammonium sulphate. An excess of sodium hydroxide is added, and the ammonia is distilled in steam (apparatus, *Figure 66*), absorbed in 2 per cent boric acid and titrated with 0·01N-hydrochloric (or -sulphuric) acid against screened methyl red. (The method is unreliable for compounds containing nitrogen in an oxidized form, e.g. as -NO$_2$, -NO, -N:N-, etc., and for nitrogen heterocycles such as pyridine.)

References

Method:
cf. MA and ZUAZAGA, *Industr. Engng Chem. (Anal.)*, 1942, **14**, 280.

Apparatus:
MARKHAM, *Biochem. J.*, 1942, **36**, 790.

Procedure

The experiment should be completed in one day. In the morning, the determination is practised on an ammonium salt until three concordant results are obtained. Digestion of the organic compound can then be performed mid-day and the distillation and titration of the ammonia in the afternoon.

The practice determination: ammonia distillation

Dissolve 'AnalaR' ammonium sulphate (*ca.* 20 mg; weighed accurately, see p 125) in distilled water in a 50-c.c. graduated flask, and make up the volume to the mark. Meanwhile, steam out the apparatus (*Figure 66*) (A. Gallenkamp and Co. Ltd) for 5–10 minutes with the screw clips *a* and *c* shut. Then open the clips *c* and *a* and remove the burner from beneath the steam generator *b*. Pipette a 5·0-c.c. portion of the ammonium sulphate solution into the funnel *f*, raise the stopper momentarily to allow the solution to run into the vessel *e*, rinse the funnel *f* with distilled water (2 × 2·5 c.c.), and run the rinsings into *e*. Place a 100-c.c. conical flask containing 2 per cent boric acid solution (5·0 c.c.) and 4 *drops* of screened indicator (10 c.c. of 0·1 per cent bromocresol green plus 4 c.c. of 0·1 per cent methyl red, each in 95 per cent ethanol) on a cork support so that the solution covers the tip of the condenser (as shown in *Figure 66*). Pour aqueous sodium hydroxide (40 per cent, 5·0 c.c.) into the funnel *f*. Raise the stopper in *f* slightly for a moment, to allow the alkali to run into *e*. Replace the burner under the steam generator *b* and close the clips *a* and *c*. From time to time, run off, by cautiously opening the clip *c*, the condensate which collects in the outer vessel *d*. When about 25 c.c. of distillate have been collected, lower the

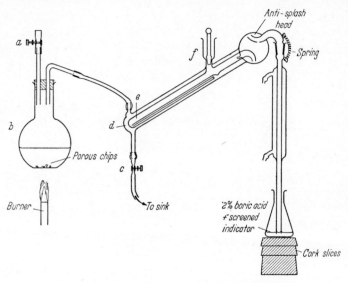

*Figure 66. Apparatus for ammonia distillation
(Kjeldahl determination of nitrogen)*

conical flask (by removing a section of the cork support) so that the condenser no longer touches the liquid, and collect a further 10 c.c. of distillate. Rinse the end of the condenser with a little distilled water into the conical flask. Place distilled water (5 c.c.) in the funnel *f* and remove the burner from beneath the steam generator *b*. Shortly afterwards, the contents of *e* siphon into *d*. At once open the screw clip *c*, and, as soon as the solution has run out from *d*, close the clip *c*. Raise the stopper in *f* momentarily so that the water in the funnel flows into *e* and then siphons into *d*. Then run the washings out at *c* and close the clip *c* again. Without delay, by the same procedure, rinse the vessel *e* twice more with 5-c.c. portions of distilled water, added from the funnel *f*. The apparatus is then ready (without further steaming) for the next distillation.

Titrate the contents of the 100-c.c. conical flask with 0·01N-hydrochloric or -sulphuric acid, added from a 10-c.c. micro-burette. The blue colour of the indicator changes sharply to grey at the end-point. (The indicator is pink in acid.)

Repeat the determination on further portions of the ammonium sulphate solution until three concordant results are obtained.

Determination of nitrogen in an organic compound

Weigh (to 0·01 mg) portions of the compound (each containing *ca.* 0·4 mg of nitrogen) into two micro-weighing-pots (see p 126). Drop these carefully into separate, clean, dry digestion flasks. To each flask add powdered selenium (*ca.* 3 mg), and copper sulphate pentahydrate–potassium sulphate mixture (3/1; *ca.* 5 mg), followed by micro-analytical reagent grade sulphuric acid (1·0 c.c.). Add the same amounts of catalysts and of sulphuric acid to each of two other clean, dry digestion flasks ('blanks'). Heat the

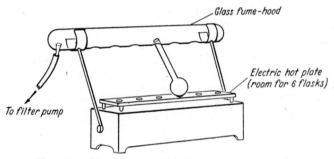

Figure 67. Digestion stand (Kjeldahl determination of nitrogen)

four flasks on the electric digestion stand (*Figure 67*) (A. Gallenkamp and Co. Ltd) so that the acid refluxes gently. Connect the glass fume-hood to the filter-pump. The acid darkens and then becomes colourless: continue digestion for 1 hour longer. Cool the flasks, add distilled water (2 c.c.) to each, and cool the flasks again.

Subject the contents of each flask in turn to the ammonia distillation and titration procedure.

Subtract the mean of the titration values for the two 'blank' determinations on the reagents from each of the other two titration values. From the two results, calculate the percentage of nitrogen in the organic compound. The determinations should agree to within 0·4 of a unit.

23

ESTIMATION OF ACTIVE HYDROGEN

(I) ZEREWITINOFF'S METHOD, AND (II) BY LITHIUM ALUMINIUM HYDRIDE

INTRODUCTION

COMPOUNDS which contain reactive hydrogen atoms, such as are present in the groupings -OH, -SH, -NH$_2$, -CO$_2$H, -CO·NH$_2$, -CO·CH$_2$·CO-, -C≡CH, -CH=CH·CH$_2$·CH=CH-, etc., are attacked by Grignard reagents with the formation of hydrocarbons. The estimation of active hydrogen by an adaptation of this general reaction (Zerewitinoff's method) has importance in structure elucidation.

The compound is treated in an inert atmosphere with an excess of methylmagnesium iodide in a vessel attached to a gas burette (see *Figure 71*), and the volume of gas evolved is measured

$$R·H + MeMgI \longrightarrow RMgI + CH_4$$

According to this reaction scheme, 1 mole of methane is evolved per atom of active hydrogen. Thus 1 mg mole of a compound produces 22·4 c.c. of gas at s.t.p. for each active hydrogen atom.

Diamyl ether, anisole, xylene and pyridine are the usual reaction media; a temperature of 90° may be required for completion of the reaction (heating above 90° may cause decomposition of the solvent by the Grignard reagent). If the reaction proceeds very readily at room temperature, diethyl ether (which is easy to purify) can be used.

Lithium aluminium hydride can be used in place of Grignard reagents for the estimation of active hydrogen. It reacts with evolution of hydrogen

$$4R·H + LiAlH_4 \longrightarrow R_4LiAl + 4H_2$$

The numerical results are generally similar to those obtained with Grignard reagents, except e.g. for amines and keto-enol tautomers.

The estimation can be performed with the simple Zerewitinoff apparatus (*Figure 71*). Suitable solvents for the lithium aluminium hydride reagent are dibutyl ether and *N*-ethylmorpholine, and dioxane is a permissible reaction medium.

The methods give results to ± 0.2 active hydrogen.

REFERENCES

Zerewitinoff's method:

BRAUDE and STERN, *J. chem. Soc.*, **1946**, 404.

FUCHS, ISHLER and SANDHOFF, *Industr. Engng Chem. (Anal.)*, 1940, **12**, 507.

LEHMAN and BASCH, *ibid*, 1945, **17**, 428.

SUDBOROUGH and HIBBERT, *J. chem. Soc.*, 1909, **95**, 477.

ZEREWITINOFF, *Ber. dtsch. chem. Ges.*, 1907, **40**, 2027; *cf.* TSCHUGAEFF, *ibid*, 1902, **35**, 3912.

Lithium aluminium hydride method:

HOCHSTEIN, *J. Amer. chem. Soc.*, 1949, **71**, 305.

KRYNITSKY, JOHNSON and CARHART, *ibid*, 1948, **70**, 486.

LIEB and SCHÖNIGER, *Mikrochemie*, 1950, **35**, 400.

(i) ZEREWITINOFF'S METHOD

Dry in an oven the apparatus for preparation of the Grignard reagent, the stock-bottle and the two-limbed reaction vessel. Allow a 1·5-litre beaker of water to reach temperature equilibrium with the laboratory.

Preparation of the Grignard reagent

Set up the apparatus as shown in *Figure 68*. Place magnesium turnings (2 g; dried for 10 minutes in the oven) in the flask and pour into the tap-funnel a solution of methyl iodide (12 g; 5·25 c.c.) in anisole* (50 c.c.; dried by distillation from sodium). Run about one quarter of the solution into the flask and start the reaction by rubbing the turnings against the bottom of the flask with a glass rod (care). Add the remainder of the methyl iodide solution during 30 minutes, and then heat the reaction mixture on the steam-bath for 1 hour. Distil off unreacted methyl iodide in a current of dry nitrogen (see *Figure 69*), by heating the flask on the steam-bath for 15 minutes. Free the nitrogen from traces of oxygen by passage through a reducing solution [sodium hydrosulphite (8 g), sodium hydroxide (7·5 g) and sodium anthraquinone-2-sulphonate ('silver salt') (0·4 g) in water (50 c.c.)] and

---

* Anisole is easily purified but only a moderately good general solvent; pyridine is a much better general solvent but difficult to purify.

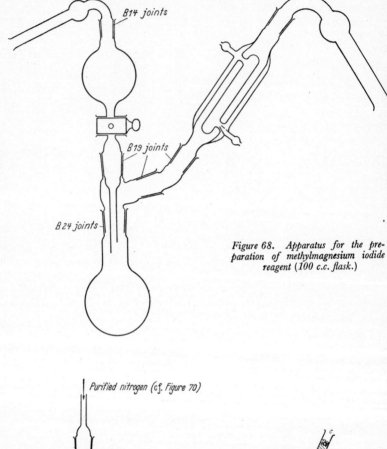

Figure 68. Apparatus for the preparation of methylmagnesium iodide reagent (100 c.c. flask.)

Figure 69. Removal of excess of methyl iodide from methylmagnesium iodide reagent

then dry the nitrogen by passage through concentrated sulphuric acid and anhydrous calcium chloride (see *Figure 70*).

Cool the solution of methylmagnesium iodide and filter it into the stock-bottle through a loose glass-wool plug in a filter-funnel. Displace the air in the stock-bottle and in the funnel by nitrogen during this operation. Close the bottle with a rubber bung.

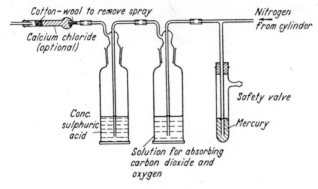

Figure 70. Nitrogen purification train

The estimation

Accurately weigh into a boat or an ampoule (see p 125) the dried substance (100–200 mg) which must be soluble in anisole. Introduce the boat or ampoule with contents into one limb of the reaction vessel *b* (*Figure 71*) and pipette in dry anisole (3·5 c.c.). When the substance has dissolved (gentle shaking or warming may be necessary), displace the air in the vessel by nitrogen, and pipette methylmagnesium iodide solution (or suspension) (10·0 c.c.) into the second limb. Fill the pipette by suction from a filter-pump through pressure tubing which carries a screw clip. Fit in place the top part of the reaction vessel (joint lightly greased) and attach the safety springs. Connect the outlet tube *c* to the gas burette by a short length of pressure tubing, and remove the barrel of the tap *d*. Pass nitrogen through the reaction vessel, via the tap *a*, for several minutes. With tap *a* closed, place the reaction vessel in the room-temperature water-bath and, after 10 minutes, replace the tap barrel at *d* and turn the tap so that the burette is open to the air. Fill the burette with dibutyl phthalate by raising the reservoir, and close the tap *d*. Lower the reservoir and turn the tap *d* so as to connect the burette to the reaction vessel. Remove the water-bath and cautiously

141

mix the solutions in the two limbs of the reaction vessel by tilting the vessel slowly from side to side, until gas evolution ceases. If necessary, heat the vessel and contents to 90° in a hot water-bath to complete the reaction.

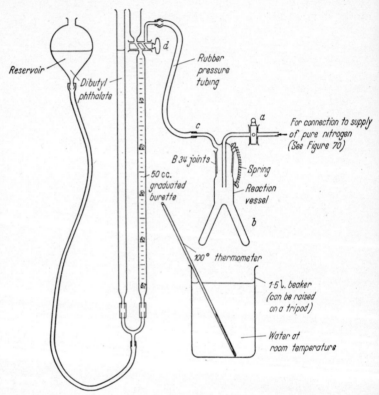

Figure 71. Apparatus for estimation of active hydrogen

Place the reaction vessel (cooled to approximately room temperature) in the room-temperature water-bath, and, after 10 minutes, level the reservoir against the dibutyl phthalate in the gas burette and read the gas volume together with the temperature and the barometric pressure. Reduce the gas volume to s.t.p.

Clean and dry the apparatus and repeat the determination.

Clean and dry the apparatus. Determine the volume of gas evolved from the anisole (3·5-c.c. portions) by the Grignard solution (10·0-c.c. portions). Calculate the mean 'blank' at s.t.p.

Subtract the 'blank' from each gas volume and calculate the percentage of active hydrogen in the substance from each value. Then deduce the number of active hydrogen atoms if the molecular weight of the substance is known.

Clean and dry the apparatus.

(ii) LITHIUM ALUMINIUM HYDRIDE METHOD

Preparation of the reagent

Powder lumps of lithium aluminium hydride (2–3 g) under dibutyl ether (dried by distillation from sodium) and transfer the slurry to an 8-oz. reagent bottle with dibutyl ether (total 200 c.c.). Close the bottle with a rubber bung which carries a bunsen valve (see *Figure 72*), and shake the bottle mechanically for 15–60 minutes.

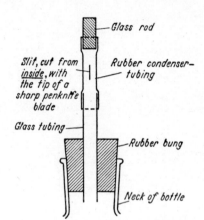

Figure 72. Bunsen valve (It is most important that the slit in the rubber tube be cut from the inside)

Decant the solution through a sintered-glass suction-filter (10 cm diameter) into a clean dry stock-bottle. Displace the air above the solution with nitrogen and close the bottle with a bung fitted with a bunsen valve.

The estimation

Perform the estimation in duplicate similarly to that with the Grignard reagent, but with *ca.* 50-mg portions of the unknown substance in dry dibutyl ether (3·0–5·0 c.c.), and 4·0-c.c. portions of lithium aluminium hydride solution. Determine the solvent 'blank' and calculate the results from each corrected gas volume.

Clean and dry the apparatus.

24

ESTIMATION OF MOLECULAR WEIGHT

INTRODUCTION

THE evaluation of molecular weight is important in structure elucidation. A variety of methods is available so that all classes of organic compounds can be examined.

Three simple methods, which depend in principle on the osmotic properties of solutions, are described here.

Rast's method

This is suitable for substances which are soluble in molten camphor, are stable up to 190°, and have molecular weights up to 300–400. The method consists of measuring the depression which is produced in the melting point of camphor by a known concentration of the substance. As camphor has a high depression constant (*ca.* 40,000) a thermometer graduated in 0·2° suffices. The method is accurate to 5–10 per cent and requires only 1–5 mg of the substance.

Boiling point (ebullioscopic) method

The elevation in the boiling point of a solvent produced by a known concentration of the substance is measured with a Beckmann thermometer. This can be read to < 0·01°. The modified Cottrell's apparatus (*Figure 75*) effectively prevents superheating of the solution. The method is applicable to stable substances with molecular weights up to *ca.* 550: it requires 25–50 mg of the substance and gives results accurate to within ± 15 per cent.

Isothermic distillation method (Barger's method)

A pair of solutions, separated by a small air space, is sealed in each of three capillary ampoules. One solution of each pair is of the unknown substance at a known concentration. The other solution of each pair is of a substance of known molecular weight at a known concentration which is different in each case. A difference in vapour pressure between the solutions of a pair, due to their different molarities, causes a slow distillation of the solvent from one solution to the other and the positions of the

144

menisci change. From a plot of the movements against molarity of the known solutions, the molarity of the unknown solution is interpolated: since the concentration is known, the molecular weight can be calculated.

The method is more accurate and more widely applicable than the preceding methods and can be used for compounds of molecular weight up to *ca.* 1000. In particular, for sensitive compounds, it is simpler and more accurate than Beckmann's freezing point method, which is adequately described elsewhere.

REFERENCES

FINDLAY, *Practical Physical Chemistry*, Longmans, Green and Co., London, 1954.
CHERONIS, *Technique of Organic Chemistry*, Interscience Publishers, Inc., New York, 1954, Vol. VI, Chapter 4.

(i) RAST'S METHOD: SEMI-MICRO

Clean chemically and dry (see p 58) a soft glass test-tube (6 × ¾ in.). Collapse and draw out the tube in a fierce flame to form a thin-walled tube *ca.* 5–6 mm diameter. Seal off the thin tube near one end, avoiding the formation of a thick blob of glass. (Excess of glass can be drawn off: touch the heated glass with a glass rod and quickly withdraw the rod to which some of the glass adheres.)

Weigh accurately into the tube *ca.* 5 mg of substance and then *ca.* 50 mg of camphor (micro-analytical reagent grade). Use a plunger-type weighing-stick (see p 126). At once seal off the tube *ca.* 3 cm from the bottom, in a micro-burner flame, and seal the tip of the bulb so formed to a m.pt tube 5–10 cm long (see *Figure 73*). Dip the bulb into medicinal paraffin at 185° and rotate the bulb to mix the contents. Repeat the melting and mixing process several times.

Introduce a little of the camphor into the bottom of a wide m.pt tube (2–3 mm diameter) and seal the tube off to form a bulb *ca.* 3 cm long. Seal a m.pt tube to the tip of the bulb to form a handle.

By means of a small rubber-band, attach both bulbs by the handles to a thermometer (145–205°) which is graduated in 0·1 or 0·2° (W. and J. George and Becker, Alperton, Middlesex). The bulbs must be on a level with the bulb of the thermometer. Mount the thermometer in a bath of medicinal paraffin (see *Figure 73*) and raise the temperature, finally very slowly.

Observe the contents of the bulbs through a lens and, when the *very last* crystals in the mixture melt, note the temperature. Similarly take the m.pt of the camphor. Repeat the observations until concordant results are obtained.

Calculate the molecular weight M of the substance from the expression

$$M = w\,M'(k - d)/Wd$$

where w = weight of substance in g, W = weight of camphor in g, M' = molecular weight of camphor (152), d = depression of m.pt in $C°$ and $k = K/M'$ where K is the ordinary depression constant.

Determine K for the camphor, if necessary, with pure naphthalene as a standard $(M = 128)$.

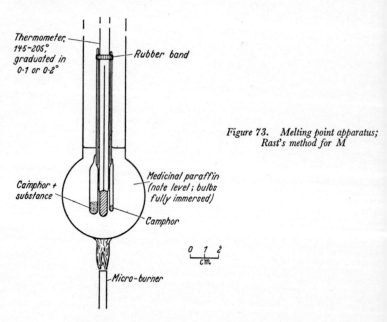

Figure 73.   *Melting point apparatus; Rast's method for M*

(ii) BOILING POINT (EBULLIOSCOPIC) METHOD

(*cf.* COTTRELL, *J. Amer. chem. Soc.*, 1919, **41**, 721; DAVIS, *J. chem. Educ.*, 1933, **10**, 47; GORDON, *ibid*, p 489; MENZIES and WRIGHT, *J. Amer. chem. Soc.*, 1921, **43**, 2314.)

Select a solvent (e.g. acetone, benzene, dioxane, toluene or nitrobenzene) for the substance. Heat medicinal paraffin (100 c.c.) in a 150-c.c. beaker to the temperature at which the selected solvent boils, and adjust the Beckmann thermometer so that the mercury thread is on the lower portion of the scale when the bulb is immersed in the paraffin. The Elliott differential thermometer (Beckmann type) (H. J. Elliott Ltd, Treforest, Glamorgan) is particularly easy to set: Invert the thermometer (*Figure 74*) and

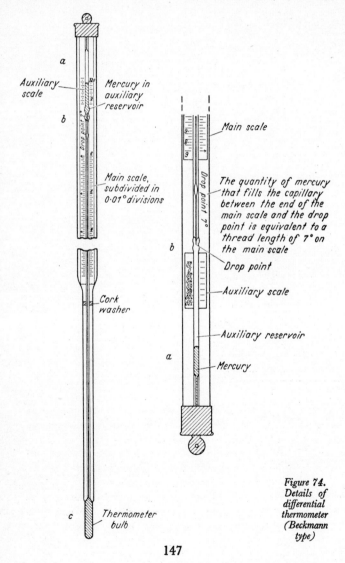

Figure 74.
Details of differential thermometer (Beckmann type)

swing it gently backwards and forwards once or twice *only* with the top towards the floor; the mercury then runs through the fine capillary *b* and drops into the reservoir *a*. When the level in the reservoir has risen above the end of the capillary *b*, gently return the thermometer to the upright position and keep it steady. The mercury runs slowly back to the bulb *c*. When the level in the

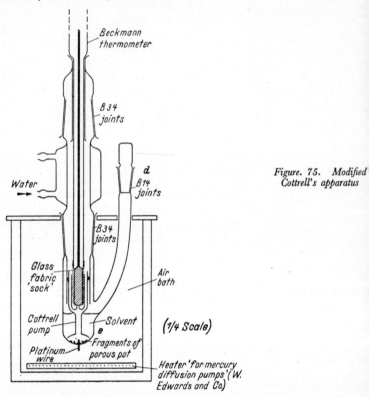

Figure. 75. *Modified Cottrell's apparatus*

reservoir *a* has fallen to the required point (the auxiliary scale is, however, marked only from − 20° to + 120°) sharply turn the thermometer to a horizontal position and back to the upright position. The mercury thread breaks and the excess of mercury remains in the reservoir. If, when the bulb *c* is heated to the required temperature, the mercury thread comes too high up the main scale, invert the thermometer and allow mercury to drop through the capillary *b* into the reservoir *a*. Then return the thermometer to the upright position. If the mercury thread is too low down on the main scale, repeat the operations from the beginning.

Wipe the Beckmann thermometer and assemble the apparatus as in *Figure 75**. Weigh or pipette the solvent (*ca.* 20 g) into the tube *e* via the side arm *d* and replace the stopper. Control the electric heater by means of the rheostat so that the liquid boils and pumps steadily over the bulb of the Beckmann thermometer. Tap the thermometer at intervals to prevent sticking of the very fine mercury thread. When after *ca.* 10 minutes the temperature (b.pt) becomes almost constant, take the scale readings at 30-second intervals during 5 minutes and calculate the mean value. If there is a slight drift in temperature repeat the readings after a further 5–10 minutes. Read the barometric pressure.

Weigh *ca.* 100 mg of the substance ($M < 550$) into a micro weighing-bucket (see p 126) and carefully slide this down the side tube *d* into the solvent, and replace the stopper. After 10 minutes, tap the thermometer at intervals and take readings as before. Calculate the elevation in the boiling point. Check the barometric pressure.

Make a known addition of the solute (*ca.* 50 mg) to the solution in *e* and determine the new elevation in boiling point.

From each set of observations, calculate a value for M for the solute from the expression

$$M = Kw/eW$$

where w = weight of substance in g, W = weight of solvent in g, e = elevation in b.pt in C° and K = the elevation constant, given in

Table III. Boiling Point Elevation Constants

(LANDOLT-BÖRNSTEIN, *Physikalischchemische Tabellen*, Springer-Verlag, Berlin.)

Solvent	B.pt at 760 mm	K
Acetone	56·3°	*ca.* 1720
Benzene	80·2°	*ca.* 2570
Dioxane	101°	*ca.* 3200
Nitrobenzene	210·9°	*ca.* 5270

Table III. It is wisest to determine K for the solvent, using pure naphthalene ($M = 128$)as standard.

If the barometric pressure changes significantly during the determination, calculate M from the expression

$$M = Kw/e'W$$

---

* The glass fabric 'sock' on the thermometer bulb helps to eliminate small temperature fluctuations (MAGEE and WILSON, *Analyst*, 1948, **73**, 597).

149

where $e' = e - (dB . K)/(B . M')$ and $dB =$ increase in barometric pressure in mm, $B =$ mean barometric pressure in mm of mercury, and $M' =$ molecular weight of the solvent in the vapour state at the boiling point.

(iii) Isothermic Distillation Method (Barger's Method)

(*cf.* Niederl, Kasanof, Kisch and Subba Rao, *Mikrochemie*, 1949, **34**, 132.)

Make up e.g. in methanol or acetone a 0·015–0·045m-solution of the substance, i.e. weigh 50 mg of the substance (M, 110–330) into a 10-c.c. standard flask or 5 mg into a 1·0-c.c. flask.

Dissolve 455 mg of azobenzene ('for chromatographic standardization', British Drug Houses Ltd) in methanol in a 50-c.c. standard flask. Make dilutions of this 0·05m-solution to give 0·025m- and 0·01m-solutions. These solutions will serve for a large number of estimations.

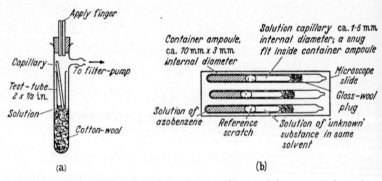

Figure 76. (a) *Introduction of a solution into a capillary (sealed at one end) by suction;* (b) *Solution capillaries mounted for observation of meniscus movements*

Select a length ($\not< 36$ cm) of uniform*, narrow-bore tubing (1·0–1·5 mm internal diameter) which fits *snugly* inside a piece of wider-bore tubing. Cut the narrow tubing into six 6-cm lengths and the wider tubing into three 8-cm lengths. Seal one end of every piece of tube.

Introduce a 2·5-cm length of the unknown solution into each of three of the narrow-bore tubes, with a capillary dropper or by

---

* To ensure uniformity, measure the internal diameter at each end of the tubing with e.g. a scale graduated in tenths of a mm, with attached magnifying glass (Huhag, Berlin). This method is sufficiently accurate.

suction [apparatus, see *Figure 76*(a)], and centrifuge the liquid down to the sealed end (hand centrifuge, *Figure 40*). Seal the open end of each capillary. Similarly seal up a 2·5-cm length of azobenzene solution in each of the remaining three narrow-bore tubes, a solution of different strength in each tube.

Cut the top off one of the 'unknown' solution capillaries (with the sharp edge of a piece of broken tile) 3–4 mm above the meniscus and slide the capillary, sealed end first, into one of the wider-bore tubes. Similarly, open one of the azobenzene solution capillaries, and push this, open end first, into the same container tube as far as it will go [see *Figure 76*(b)]. (It is important that the inner tubes fit into the outer ones as closely as possible and that the open end of each inner tube has been cut squarely.) Push in a small wad of glass-wool to keep the capillaries in place and rapidly seal off the end of the container-tube in a very small hot flame, so that heat does not reach the solutions. Make a reference mark on the container-tube with a diamond point somewhere between the positions of the menisci. Mount the container-tube on a microscope slide with 2 drops of sodium silicate solution (sp. gr. 1·7). In the same manner, make up and mount on the same slide the other two container-tubes, each containing an 'unknown' solution capillary and one of the azobenzene solution capillaries [see *Figure 76*(b)].

Keep the capillaries at a roughly constant room-temperature.

After 24 hours, place the slide under a microscope fitted with a mechanical stage and a cross-wire eyepiece, or under a travelling microscope (C. Baker of Holborn Ltd, London) and measure, for each tube, the distance of the apex of each meniscus from the reference mark. Repeat the measurements 48 hours later. (For higher boiling solvents the time between observations must be extended perhaps to several weeks.)

For each tube find from the measurements the change in position of the 'unknown' solution meniscus and the change in position of the azobenzene solution meniscus, giving the changes their correct signs: $+$ towards reference mark, $-$ away. Subtract each pair of values and divide by 2. Tabulate the observations:

Tube No.	Meniscus change for 'unknown' solution	Meniscus change for azobenzene solution	Corrected change	Azobenzene concentration M
1	e.g. $+x$	$-y$	$\frac{1}{2}\{x-(-y)\}$	0·01
2	0	0	0	0·025
3	$-p$	$+q$	$\frac{1}{2}\{-p-(+q)\}$	0·05

L

151

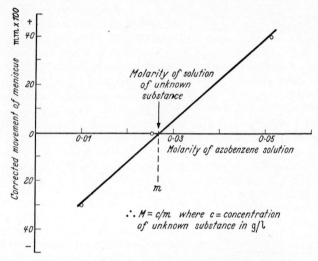

Figure 77. Deduction of molecular weight (Barger's method)

Plot the corrected changes as ordinates against molar strengths of the azobenzene solutions as abscissae. The molar strength of the unknown solution is given by the abscissa for zero change, and M can then be calculated (see *Figure 77*).

25

POTENTIOMETRIC TITRATION

INTRODUCTION

THE change in hydrogen ion concentration which accompanies the neutralization of an acid or a base is better followed potentiometrically than with indicators. The pH of the solution (which may be non-aqueous[1]) is determined at intervals during the titration by measuring with a valve potentiometer the e.m.f. of a cell comprising, for example, a glass electrode (potential proportional to the pH), the solution, and a calomel reference electrode (fixed potential). The potentiometer is calibrated to read in pH. From the plot of pH against c.c. of standard solution added, the end-point(s) can be found accurately (methods, see below): in the region of an end-point, the pH changes rapidly and the curve shows an inflection (see *Figure 79*).

Potentiometric titration has important applications in organic chemistry. The method is readily adaptable to micro titration[2] and makes possible the titration of very weak acids and bases[1] and of acids and bases at high dilution or in the presence of coloured materials, oxidizing agents and colloids. The titration curve gives the number of titratable groups. From the end-points, equivalent weights and thence possible molecular weight of an organic acid or base can be deduced, as well as the acid or base strengths and the degrees of ionization of the functional groups. The determination of equivalents is necessary in structure elucidation work and may be used to assess the purity of compounds[3]. A knowledge of pK values has proved fundamental to the study of the tautomerism and fine structure of nitrogenous bases[4], and is necessarily involved in theories of aromaticity in unsaturated nitrogen heterocycles[5] and in the correlation of structure with therapeutic activity[6].

REFERENCES

FURMAN, *Industr. Engng Chem. (Anal.)*, 1942, **14**, 367.

KOLTHOFF and LAITINEN, *pH and Electro Titrations*, John Wiley and Sons, Inc., New York, 1944.

MACINNES, *The Principles of Electrochemistry*, Reinhold Publishing Corpn, New York, 1939.

WEISSBERGER, *Technique of Organic Chemistry*, Interscience Publishers, Inc., New York, 1949, Vol. I, Part II, Chapter 27.

[1] FRITZ, *Acid–Base Titrations in Non-aqueous Solutions*, The G. Frederick Smith Chemical Company, Columbus, 1952; PRELOG, WIESNER, INGOLD and HÄFLIGER, *Helv. chim. Acta*, 1948, **31**, 1325; RUEHLE, *Industr. Engng Chem. (Anal.)*, 1938, **10**, 130.

[2] CATCH, COOK and KITCHENER, *J. chem. Soc.*, **1945**, 319; INGOLD, *Helv. chim. Acta*, 1946, **29**, 1929; STOCK, *Analyst*, 1948, **73**, 321.

[3] e.g. ALBERT, *Quart. Rev. chem. Soc., Lond.*, 1952, **6**, 197.

[4] e.g. ANGYAL and ANGYAL, *J. chem. Soc.*, **1952**, 1461.

[5] e.g. ALBERT, GOLDACRE and PHILLIPS, *ibid*, **1948**, 2240.

[6] e.g. ALBERT, *Chem. & Ind.*, **1951**, 922.

TITRATION OF ORGANIC ACIDS AND BASES

Apparatus

The apparatus (Cambridge pH Indicator 44239 with calomel reference electrode 42526/6 and sealed glass electrode 42518/2, Cambridge Instrument Co. Ltd, London) is set up as in *Figure 78*.

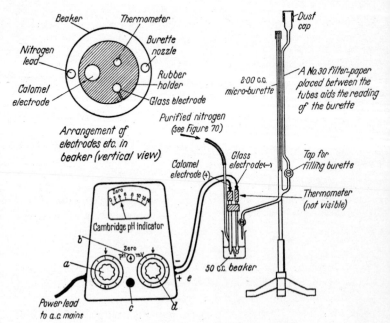

Figure 78. Apparatus for potentiometric titration

If the glass electrode has been stored dry, mount it in 0·1N-hydrochloric acid for 24 hours before use. The electrode is fragile: take great care not to touch the glass bulb against the side or bottom of the beaker.

Make sure that the switch *b* of the pH Indicator is at 'zero' and then connect the instrument to the electricity supply. After 5 minutes turn the 'set to zero' control *c* so that the Indicator pointer reads 'zero' (actually marked at pH 4). Rinse the glass electrode with distilled water, remove the rubber cap from the calomel electrode and mount the electrodes, together with the small thermometer, in the rubber holder: the rubber is slit at one hole to facilitate insertion of the glass electrode. Connect the electrode stand to earth (e.g. a water pipe).

Standardization

Put *ca.* 20 c.c. of the pH 4·0 buffer solution (0·05M-potassium hydrogen phthalate) in a clean 50-c.c. beaker and raise the beaker on cork slices so that the sintered tip of the calomel reference electrode and the lower bulb of the glass electrode are immersed.

Connect the electrodes to the pH Indicator: push the plugs right home in their sockets at *e*. Set the 'solution temperature °C' control *a* to the temperature of the buffer solution and turn the switch *b* from 'zero' to 'pH'. Adjust the 'set to buffer pH' control *d* so that the Indicator pointer reads 4·00. Then return the switch *b* to 'zero'. Remove and rinse the beaker, rinse the electrodes with distilled water and replace the beaker, now containing *ca.* 20 c.c. of the pH 9·27 buffer solution (0·05M-sodium borate). Turn the switch *b* to 'pH' and the 'solution temperature °C' control *a* to the temperature of the buffer solution: the pH Indicator should read the correct pH. Do not move the 'set to buffer pH' control. Return the switch *b* to 'zero', remove the beaker and rinse the electrodes and the thermometer. Gently blot the ends of the electrodes and the thermometer with filter-paper.

Restandardize the instrument each day.

Titration

Weigh accurately (see p 125) *ca.* 5 mg of the organic acid or base into a clean 50-c.c. beaker, dissolve the compound in distilled water (20 c.c.), by warming if necessary, bring the solution to room temperature and put the beaker in position (see *Figure 78*). Insert a capillary tube between the electrodes in the centre of the beaker and pass a steady stream of purified nitrogen through

155

(see p 139 and *Figure 70*) to stir the contents of the beaker and to remove dissolved carbon dioxide. Turn the switch *b* to 'pH', adjust the 'solution temperature °C' control *a* and, after 1 minute, note the reading on the pH Indicator. From a 2·00-c.c. micro-burette (e.g. the Gallenkamp type, Catalogue No. 2754, which is easy to fill and has a ground nozzle that delivers micro drops) add 0·10 c.c. of 0·05N-sodium hydroxide or -hydrochloric acid as appropriate. Keep the burette nozzle away from the side of the beaker, etc. After 1 minute, read the pH. Add further portions of the standard alkali or acid (0·1 c.c. or less) and 1 minute after each addition note the pH. Plot pH against c.c. of standard solution, as the observations are made, and alter the volume of the added portions of alkali or acid to keep the points on the curve spaced fairly evenly (see *Figure 79*). Continue the titration until the pH no longer alters much with the addition of the standard solution.

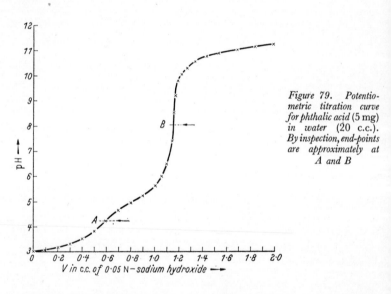

Figure 79. *Potentiometric titration curve for phthalic acid (5 mg) in water (20 c.c.). By inspection, end-points are approximately at A and B*

Turn off the nitrogen. Move the switch *b* to 'zero' and disconnect the electricity supply and the electrodes from the pH Indicator. Remove the beaker, rinse the electrodes and the thermometer with distilled water, put the rubber cap on the end of the calomel electrode and mount the glass electrode (care) in distilled water. Empty and rinse the burette. Replace all the covers.

Determination of the equivalence or end-point(s)

There are several more accurate methods of determining the end-point(s) than by inspection of the inflections on the titration curve.

(a) *Rate of change in slope of the titration curve*—Choose 4–5 points on each side of the approximate end-point and plot $(\Delta pH/\Delta V)$ against V as indicated in *Figure 80*(a). Choose for ΔV a small value, e.g. 0·04 c.c. The intercept from the maximum on to the abscissa gives the end-point in units of V.

The sharpness of the maximum and hence the accuracy of the method depends directly on the sharpness of the inflection on the titration curve.

(b) *Gran's method*—(cf. *Analyst*, 1952, **77**, 661; *Acta chem. scand.*, 1950, **4**, 559). Plot the appropriate functions against V:

E.g. For strong acid against strong base

before end-point	$(V_0 + V) \cdot 10^{\,k-pH}$
after end-point	$(V_0 + V) \cdot 10^{pH - k}$

For weak acid against strong base

Mono-basic acid

before end-point	$V \cdot 10^{\,k-pH}$
after end-point	$(V_0 + V) \cdot 10^{pH - k}$

Di-basic acid

before first end-point	$V \cdot 10^{\,k-pH}$
after first end-point	$(V_{e_2} - V) \cdot 10^{pH - k}$
before second end-point	$(V - V_{e_1}) \cdot 10^{\,k-pH}$
after second end-point	$(V_0 + V) \cdot 10^{pH - k}$

where V = c.c. of standard alkali; V_0 = c.c. of original solution; V_e = c.c. of standard alkali added when the equivalence point (estimated by inspection) is reached; and k = an arbitrary constant (most conveniently the nearest integer to the pH value at the approximate end-point).

The plot gives two straight lines. The intercept from their point of intersection on to the abscissa gives the end-point in units of V (see *Figure 81*).

Gran's method has a somewhat wider applicability than method (a) but fails for very weak acids and bases. In such cases an approximate value for the

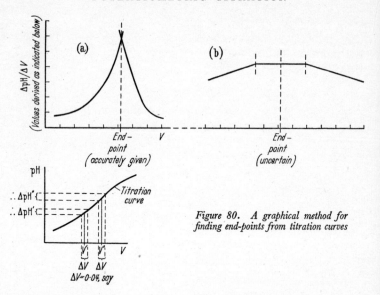

Figure 80. A graphical method for finding end-points from titration curves

end-point can be obtained by plotting $(\Delta pH/\Delta V)$ against V and bisecting the long flat maximum [see *Figure 80* (b)]. It is usually better to change the solvent so as to enhance the acid or base strength of the compound to be titrated.

Record the number of functional groups titrated and the accurate equivalence point(s) and calculate the equivalent(s) of the organic acid or base.

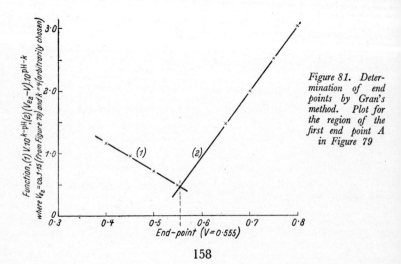

Figure 81. Determination of end points by Gran's method. Plot for the region of the first end point A in Figure 79

Determination of pK *values*

Obtain pK values for the acid or base function(s) corresponding to the equivalence or neutralization point(s) by one of the following methods:

(a) *Acids* (strong–moderately weak)—titrated with a strong base. From the accurate end-point(s) and the titration curve determine the pH at the half-neutralization point(s). At half-neutralization, [salt] = [organic acid], whence from the Henderson equation

$$pH = pk_a + \log_{10} [salt]/[organic\ acid] \qquad . \qquad (1)$$

we have $pk_a = pH$.

This method gives good results for not too dilute solutions in the range pH 4–10.

k_a (described by the pk_a value $= -\log_{10} k_a$) is the classical dissociation constant for the organic acid.

The titration reaction is $HA + OH^- \rightleftharpoons H_2O + A^-$ where $[A^-] = [salt]$ and $[HA] = [organic\ acid]$: the *added* hydroxyl ions are consumed at once so that $[OH^-]$ is merely that due to the dissociation of water. Subtracting $H^+ + OH^- \rightleftharpoons H_2O$ we have $HA - H^+ \rightleftharpoons A^-$ or $HA \rightleftharpoons H^+ + A^-$ (which represents the dissociation of the organic acid) whence

$$\frac{[H^+][A^-]}{[HA]} = k_a = \frac{[H^+][salt]}{[organic\ acid]},$$

the logarithmic form of which is the Henderson equation.

The symbols K_a and pK_a are employed in connection with the extended definition of an acid. $K_a = k_a$ but K_a has the wider meaning in that it relates to the dissociation not only of free acids, but also of conjugate acids, i.e. salts of weak bases with strong acids.

(b) *Bases* (strong–moderately weak)—titrated with a strong acid. Similarly, from the accurate end-point(s) and the titration curve determine the pH at the half-neutralization point(s). There, [salt] = [organic base], whence from the equation

$$pH = pK_a + \log_{10} [organic\ base]/[salt] \qquad . \qquad (2)$$

we have $pK_a = pH$.

K_a (described by the pK_a value) is the acidity constant of the organic base with respect to the dissociation of its conjugate acid, $BH^+ \rightleftharpoons B + H^+$ (i.e. the reverse of the titration reaction) whence

$$\frac{[B][H^+]}{[BH^+]} = K_a = \frac{[organic\ base][H^+]}{[salt]}$$

Alternatively, for strong bases, the strength is defined by the symbols K_b and pK_b where K_b is the equilibrium constant for the dissociation of the base hydroxide $BOH \rightleftharpoons B^+ + OH^-$ (where $B = NHMe_3$, etc.). Hence $K_b = [B^+][OH^-]/[BOH]$ so that

$$pK_b = pOH - \log [B^+]/[BOH]$$

$$= pk_w - pH + \log [BOH]/[B^+]$$

or $pK_b = pk_w - pH + \log$ [base]/[salt] with reference to the titration reaction [cf. (a)]. At the half-neutralization point, [base] = [salt] so that

$$pK_b = pk_w - pH \approx 14 - pH.$$

(c) *Very weak acids or bases*—Substitute in each of equations (1), or (2), respectively, values from 3–5 points chosen on the titration curve on each side of the approximate end-point. Then average the 6–10 results in order to obtain a good value for the pK. A correction for hydrolysis can be applied to pK values, e.g. for very weak bases by use of the equation

$$pK_a = pH + \log \{\tfrac{1}{2}c - [H^+]\}/\{\tfrac{1}{2}c + [H^+]\}$$

(MORLEY and SIMPSON, *J. chem. Soc.*, **1949**, 1014).

26

POLAROGRAPHIC ANALYSIS

ORGANIC compounds containing groupings which can be reduced electrolytically (e.g. -CHO, $>$CO, -NO$_2$, aliphatic halogen, and $>$C$=$C$<$ or -C$\equiv$C- conjugated to a carbonyl group) can be identified and often estimated by polarographic analysis.

A solution of the compound (10^{-2}–10^{-4}M) in water, or water and a miscible organic solvent (a lower alcohol or dioxane) containing a chloride electrolyte, e.g. ammonium chloride, is electrolysed in a cell containing a very small cathode and a mercury anode. Liberation of chloride ions at the anode precipitates mercuric chloride to form a calomel electrode (fixed potential). The cathode can be either a dropping mercury electrode (the drops are $\not>$ 0·5 mm in diameter) or a micro-platinum electrode. Different voltages are applied to the cathode, and the currents through the cell are measured, e.g. by a long period galvanometer. Alternatively, the current/voltage relation can be shown visually on the screen of a cathode ray oscillograph.

For substances containing one reducible group, the current/applied voltage curve (for a dropping mercury cathode) is usually of the type shown in *Figure 82*. At voltages below the decomposition potential of the substance a small current (residual current) is carried by the electrolyte. This current increases linearly with increase in the applied voltage. When the decomposition potential is reached, electrolysis of the substance begins and the concentration of the substance at the surface of the dropping mercury cathode decreases. Diffusion of the substance towards the cathode from the main bulk of the solution commences and the current through the cell rises. As the applied voltage is further increased, the concentration of the substance at the mercury surface becomes so small that the difference between the concentrations at the mercury surface and in the bulk of the solution approaches a constant value, which is nearly equal to the concentration of the solution. The rate of diffusion of substance towards the cathode becomes almost constant and the current which can be carried by the electrolyte reaches a maximum. This 'limiting' or 'diffusion' current is thus virtually proportional to the concentration of

161

substance in the solution. However, with organic compounds this is not always so.

The steps in the current/voltage curves for different concentrations of the same substance are each symmetrical about their mid-points (see *Figure 82*) which lie on an almost vertical line.

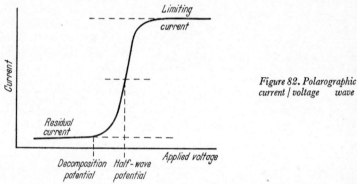

Figure 82. Polarographic current / voltage wave

The intersection of this line with the abscissa gives the half-wave potential which, being virtually independent of the concentration, is therefore characteristic of the substance.

REFERENCES

HEYROVSKY, *Polarographie*, Springer-Verlag, Vienna, 1941.

HEYROVSKY and SHIKATA, *Rec. Trav. chim. Pays-Bas*, 1925, **44**, 496 and subsequent papers.

KOLTHOFF and LINGANE, *Polarography*, Interscience Publishers, Inc., New York, 1952.

PAGE, *Quart. Rev. chem. Soc., Lond.*, 1952, **6**, 262.

WEISSBERGER, *Technique of Organic Chemistry*, Interscience Publishers, Inc., New York, 1949, Vol. I, Part II, Chapter 28.

POLAROGRAPHY OF ACETOPHENONE AND BENZOPHENONE

Dissolve acetophenone (*ca.* 10 mg; accurately weighed, see p 125) in ethanol in a 50-c.c. standard flask. Transfer 5·0 c.c. of the solution to a 50-c.c. standard flask, add 1M-ammonium chloride (5·0 c.c.) and fill up to the mark with 50 per cent (by volume) aqueous ethanol. The solution is now 10^{-4}M with respect to acetophenone and 0·1M to ammonium chloride. Prepare a 10^{-4}M-solution of benzophenone in the same manner.

Move the support of the dropping electrode of the 'Cambridge' Polarograph (see *Figure 83*) (Cambridge Instrument Co. Ltd,

London), so that the capillary e is over a 100-c.c. beaker partly filled with distilled water. Fill the mercury reservoir c to the mark with clean mercury (redistilled in conventional apparatus, under reduced pressure) and raise the reservoir to the top of the stand.

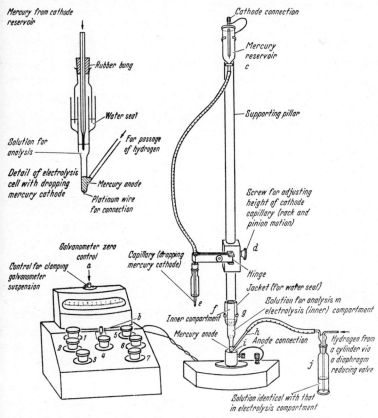

Figure 83. Apparatus for polarography. Controls: 1 damping, 2 standardize, 3 applied voltage, 4 sensitivity, 5 zero, 6 counter current, 7 cell current

After 5 minutes, lower the end of the capillary into the water by turning the knob d, and 10 minutes later check that the mercury drop rate is 1 drop/2–3 seconds. If the drop rate is outside these limits, clean the capillary with concentrated nitric acid or renew it.

Fill the small hole i in the electrolysis vessel holder with mercury, put the electrolysis vessel in position and add the solution of acetophenone (3·0 c.c.) to the inner compartment f. Lower the capillary

163

into f until the tip is 0·5 cm below the solution surface and place distilled water (depth *ca*. 1 cm) in the outer compartment g. Connect the side arm h to a Drechsel bottle j containing the ketone solution (20 c.c.) (as shown in *Figure 83*) and pass hydrogen through it into the electrolysis solution at 2 bubbles/second for 10 minutes.

In the meantime switch on the instrument, release the galvanometer suspension and, with the switch b at 'Galvo off', zero the light spot with the screw a. With the switch b at 'Standardize', adjust the 'Standardize' control until no deflection is observed. If the galvanometer cannot be brought to zero, use an arbitrary reading on the galvanometer scale as the zero-line. (If the mains a.c. supply is less than 48 c/s the instrument fails to function.) Check the standardization at intervals and make adjustments as necessary.

Set the 'Applied voltage' control to 0·4 V, the 'Sensitivity' control to 1/20 and the 'Counter current' control to zero. Turn off the hydrogen and move the switch b to 'Working'. Zero the galvanometer with the 'Zero' control and minimize the periodic oscillation of the spot with the 'Damping' control. Do not alter the 'Sensitivity' and 'Damping' settings during the experiment.

Turn the 'Applied voltage' control to 0·5 V and zero the galvanometer by turning the 'Cell current' control. Note the applied voltage and cell-current readings. Similarly, note cell-current readings at intervals of 0·1 V up to 2·0 V. Plot the cell-current (mA) against the applied voltage.

Repeat the procedure with the benzophenone solution in the polarograph cell (change the solution in the Drechsel bottle j) and plot the current/voltage curve on the same graph as the acetophenone curve. Deduce the half-wave potentials and limiting currents for the two ketones (*cf. Figure 82*).

In the same way, determine the current/voltage curve for the 'unknown' ketone solution (concentration in range $0·8 \times 10^{-4}$– $1·4 \times 10^{-4}$M). Identify the ketone from the half-wave potential and estimate its concentration from the limiting current.

Switch off the instrument, clamp the galvanometer suspension and empty, clean and dry the electrolysis cell and the Drechsel bottle. Pour the mercury into the residues bottle.

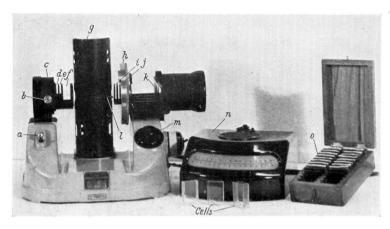

Figure 84.   Hilger 'Spekker' absorptiometer

27

COLORIMETRIC ANALYSIS

INTRODUCTION

COLORIMETRIC methods of analysis are convenient and rapid, and are increasingly used, e.g. in biochemical work, because almost any colour reaction can be adapted fairly easily to the determination of very small quantities of material. As the colour intensity is not always proportional to the concentration of the material, a calibration curve is constructed which covers the necessary range of concentration.

The intensity of the colour is measured by the extinction $E = \log_{10}(I_0/I)$ where I_0 = the intensity of the incident light and I = the intensity of the light transmitted by the coloured solution.

The extinction will be maximal if the wavelength of the incident light is close to the absorption maximum of the coloured solution. Hence colour filters are interposed in the incident light path.

Instruments for measuring E visually are relatively simple in construction but demand skill in the operator in matching colour intensities. Photoelectric instruments, of which there are two main types, are therefore generally preferable:

(a) The Hilger 'Spekker' absorptiometer (see *Figure 84*) is an example of a two-photocell instrument which, because it employs a null-point method, gives measurements independent of fluctuations in the intensity of the light source. On the left-hand side of the central lamp there is a photocell and an iris diaphragm, and on the right-hand side there is a second photocell in front of which the coloured solution is placed. Between the solution and the lamp is a variable aperture, calibrated in extinction units. The electrical outputs from the photocells are balanced by adjustment, with the iris, of the light intensity falling on the left-hand photocell. The solvent is then moved into the light path on the right-hand side, in place of the solution, and the balance is re-obtained by adjustment of the aperture calibrated in E. The E value is the extinction of the coloured solution.

(b) With a single-photocell absorptiometer, e.g. the Gallenkamp model (*Figure 86*), the currents produced by the incident light and by the transmitted light, when they fall on the photocell, are

165

measured in rapid succession. The galvanometer needle is adjusted to maximum deflection ('0' on the scale) with the 'blank' cell in the light beam. The reading on the scale with the test solution in the light path is $E \times 100$.

REFERENCES

KING, *Micro-analysis in Medical Biochemistry*, J. and A. Churchill Ltd, London, 1946.

MILTON and WATERS, *Methods of Quantitative Micro-analysis*, Edward Arnold and Co., London, 1949, Part IV.

WEISSBERGER, *Technique of Organic Chemistry*, Interscience Publishers, Inc., New York, 1949, Vol. I, Part II, Chapter 22.

DETERMINATION OF AN AROMATIC AMINE

The aryl amine at several dilutions is diazotized and coupled with either H-acid (1-amino-8-hydroxynaphthalene-3 : 6-disulphonic acid) or 1-dimethylamino-naphthalene, under defined conditions. The colour intensities are measured and plotted against the concentrations of amine. The colour intensity produced by an intermediate dilution of the amine ('unknown' solution) is then measured and the concentration determined from the calibration curve. Agreement with the actual dilution value should be within 1–2 per cent.

Weigh out accurately 12·5 mg of the amine (either sulphanilamide, arsanilic acid, *p*-aminobenzoic acid, or sulphanilic acid), and dissolve it in N-hydrochloric acid in a 50-c.c. standard flask. Make three dilutions of this solution (*ca.* 0·25 mg/c.c.) with N-hydrochloric acid to give solutions of about 0·2, 0·15 and 0·1 mg/c.c., and a fourth intermediate dilution as the 'unknown'.

Cool portions of each of the five solutions (2·0 c.c.) and a portion of N-hydrochloric acid (2·0 c.c.), contained in separate 50-c.c. conical flasks, in ice for 10 minutes, and add to each, with mixing, *freshly* prepared 0·1 per cent sodium nitrite solution (1·0 c.c.). Keep the solutions in ice for a further 20–30 minutes and then add to each 2 per cent ammonium sulphamate solution (2·0 c.c.) to destroy the excess of nitrous acid; swirl the solutions vigorously from time to time and keep them in ice. After 10–15 minutes, add a coupling reagent. *Either* add N-sodium hydroxide (4·0 c.c.) and then H-acid solution (2·0 c.c.; 1 per cent in water) *or* add 50 per cent acetic acid (4·0 c.c.) and then 1-dimethylamino-naphthalene solution (2·0 c.c.; 1 per cent in ethanol). Stopper the flasks, keep the well-mixed solutions at 0–2° in the refrigerator (2–3 hours for sulphanilamide and arsanilic acid, overnight for *p*-aminobenzoic acid and sulphanilic acid) and then measure the colour intensities, using either the Hilger 'Spekker' absorptiometer or the Gallenkamp single-photocell absorptiometer.

(a) *Hilger 'Spekker' absorptiometer*

Place the 1-cm cell, filled with distilled water, in the holder on the left-hand side of the 'Spekker' photoelectric absorptiometer at *f (Figure 84)*, a neutral heat absorbing filter (H 503) in each of the outermost slots *d* and *j* and a yellow filter (606) in each of the inner slots *e* and *i*. The filters are marked 'R' and 'L' and must be placed on the correct sides of the lamp housing *g*. The filters on the right-hand side fit into place squarely, but those on the left-hand side fit in at 45°.

Fill a 0·5-cm cell with the first (most concentrated) coloured solution and another with the amine-free solution ('blank' solution) and place these on the cell carrier *k* against its right-hand side.

Make the electrical connections, release the galvanometer suspension and switch on the instruments. Slide the cell carrier *k* so that the coloured solution comes in front of the photocell, turn the density drum *h* to zero, open the light shutter by moving the lever *l* to the left and fully open the iris diaphragm with the lever at *c*.

Make connection to the galvanometer *n* by pressing the button *a* and turn the sensitivity knob *m* until the galvanometer light spot is on the zero at the left-hand end of the scale. Then adjust the iris with the lever at *c* and the fine adjustment screw at *b* so that the light spot returns to the central zero, and release the button *a*.

Slide the solvent cell into the light path, press the button *a* (the galvanometer shows a deflection) and then turn the density drum *h* so as to bring the galvanometer light spot back to the central zero. Release the button *a* and close the light shutter *l*. Record the extinction value indicated on the drum *h*. Similarly determine the extinction of the other coloured solutions.

Plot the calibration curve (extinction *E* against concentration of amine in mg/c.c.) and from it deduce the concentration of the amine in the 'unknown' solution. Compare the result with the known concentration.

In order to check that the most suitable filter was used, obtain a light absorption curve for the azo-dyestuff: measure the extinction of the strongest of the coloured solutions, using each of the colour filters in turn. Their transmission characteristics are shown in *Figure 85*. Plot the *E* values against wavelengths.

Switch off the instruments and clamp the galvanometer suspension. Empty the cells, rinse them with distilled water and place them in their container. Replace the filters in the box *o* and put the covers on the instruments.

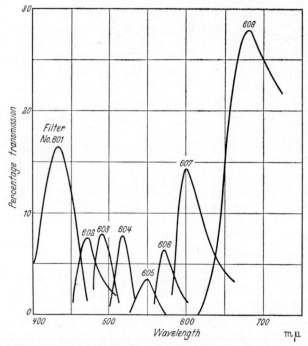

Figure 85. Light transmission characteristics of filters supplied for the Hilger 'Spekker' absorptiometer

(b) *Gallenkamp single-photocell absorptiometer*

Connect the instrument (*Figure 86*) to the electricity supply and, if necessary, set the galvanometer needle to '∞' by turning the adjustment screw with a screw-driver. Insert the heat absorbing

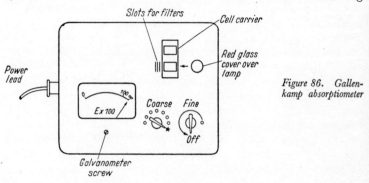

Figure 86. Gallenkamp absorptiometer

168

filter in the right-hand slot (nearest the lamp) and the green filter (Ilford 624) in the left-hand slot. Fill both the cells with water and place them in the carrier. Slide the rear cell into the light path and adjust the galvanometer reading to zero by means of the coarse and then the fine control. At once slide the front cell into the light path and read the galvanometer. This 'blank' reading corresponds to a difference between the cells in their light transmission.

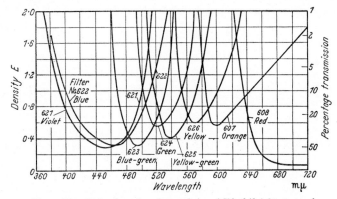

Figure 87. *Light absorption characteristics of Ilford 'bright spectrum' filters (for use with the Gallenkamp absorptiometer)*

Return the coarse control to the 'safe' position marked ★. Keep the coarse control in the 'safe' position when the instrument is not in use and always return this control to the 'safe' position whilst changing the filters and at the end of an experiment.

Fill the rear cell with the 'blank' solution, and the front cell with one of the coloured solutions.

Slide the rear cell into the light path and adjust the galvanometer to zero. Then move the front cell into the light path and read the galvanometer. Check the reading by repeating these operations.

Return the coarse control to the 'safe' position (★).

In the same way determine the galvanometer readings for the other three standard solutions and for the 'unknown' solution. Return the coarse control to the 'safe' position (★) and switch off the current.

Subtract the 'blank' reading from the values obtained for the coloured solutions and plot $E \times 100$ against the concentration of the amine. Determine the concentration of the 'unknown' solution from this calibration curve.

Obtain a rough absorption curve for the azo-dyestuff: switch on the instrument and determine $E \times 100$ for the strongest solution, using each of the colour filters in turn: before changing a filter, switch the coarse control to the 'safe' position ($*$). The *Figure 87* shows the transmission maxima of the filters. Plot $E \times 100$ against wavelength.

Finally, switch off the instrument, rinse out the cells with distilled water and return the cells and filters to their boxes.

28

ABSORPTION SPECTROMETRY

(VISUAL INSTRUMENT)

INTRODUCTION

THE determination of the light absorption properties of compounds is of very great importance for purposes of qualitative and quantitative analysis and in structure elucidation. The principles involved in the measurement and use of light absorption data are the same whether the radiation employed is in the ultraviolet $\lambda2000$–4500 Å), visible (4500–7500 Å) or infra-red region (20,000–150,000 Å or in wave numbers, 4000–*ca.* 600 cm^{-1}) although the experimental methods necessarily differ.

REFERENCES

BELLAMY, *The Infra-red Spectra of Complex Molecules*, Methuen and Co. Ltd, London, 1954.

BRAUDE, *Rep. Progr. Chem.* [*Ann. Reports*], 1945, **42**, 105.

GILLAM and STERN, *Electronic Absorption Spectroscopy*, Edward Arnold (Publishers) Ltd, London, 1954.

WEISSBERGER, *Technique of Organic Chemistry*, Interscience Publishers, Inc., New York, 1949, Vol. I, Part II, Chapter 21.

THEORY

For dilute solutions in which the light absorbing species does not change with concentration, the Beer–Lambert law holds: the fraction of incident light absorbed is proportional to the number of absorbing molecules (n) in the light path. This can be expressed as $\log_{10}(I_{\lambda_0}/I_\lambda) = nk = E$, where I_{λ_0} is the intensity of the incident light of wavelength λ, I_λ is the intensity of the light transmitted, and E is the 'extinction' or 'density'. At constant temperature, n is proportional to cl, where c is the concentration of the light absorbing species in the containing cell of length l cm. Hence $E = cl \times$ a factor. The most frequently used proportionality factors are ε the molecular extinction coefficient (with c in

171

g-moles/litre), and $E_{1cm}^{1\%}$ (with c in g/100 c.c.). We have, therefore:

$$E_{1\,cm}^{1\%} = E/cl \text{ and } \varepsilon = EM/10\,cl = E_{1\,cm}^{1\%}\,M/10$$

where c is in g/100 c.c. and M is the molecular weight of the light absorbing species.

The light absorption properties of a compound for a region of the spectrum are expressed quantitatively by the extinction or light absorption curve; λ is plotted against ε or $\log_{10} \varepsilon$, or, if M is not known, against $E_{1\,cm}^{1\%}$.

HILGER–NUTTING VISUAL SPECTROPHOTOMETER (*Figure 88*)

The principles of absorption spectrometry are perhaps most readily appreciated from the working of this instrument, which is suitable for measurements in the visible region (4500–7500 Å). It has a glass prism which gives very good dispersion.

The light from a 'Pointolite' lamp* inside the housing a is divided into two parallel beams by the lenses at c. The lower beam passes through the solution of absorbent at d and is reflected on to the slit (control at g). The upper beam passes through the solvent at d and through the two coaxial Nicol prisms of photometer e before it reaches the slit. Rotation of one polarizing prism with respect to the other reduces the intensity of the light in the upper beam: the photometer drum at e which is rotated by means of the knob f, is marked in units of E. After passing through the slit at g and a shutter h, the beams traverse a constant deviation prism at j which can be rotated by the wavelength drum i. The dispersed beams then pass through the telescope and so to the eyepiece m, one beam immediately above the other. The width of the spectrum range which is visible can be narrowed by the eyepiece slit (control at l). The reading on the drum i gives the wavelength of the light at the centre of the slit gap.

DETERMINATION OF THE LIGHT ABSORPTION CURVES OF MALACHITE GREEN AND CRYSTAL VIOLET

(*a*) Prepare approximately 0·0005 per cent weight/volume solutions of the two dyes:

---

* The lamp contains two small closely-placed tungsten balls, which are raised to incandescence by an arc between them. The balls are one behind the other in the line of the instrument so that only one is visible from the eyepiece, i.e. the lamp is virtually a point source.

Figure 88.   Hilger–Nutting visual spectrophotometer

Weigh out accurately about 12 mg of powdered malachite green into a 50-c.c. standard flask. Dissolve the dye in methanol and make up the volume of the solution to 50 c.c. Pipette a 1·0-c.c. portion of the solution into a 50-c.c. standard flask, add 1·0 c.c. of 0·1M-hydrochloric acid and make up the volume of the solution to 50 c.c. with methanol.

Prepare a solution of crystal violet in the same manner.

(b) Determine the instrument 'blanks':

Switch on the tungsten lamp of the Hilger–Nutting visual spectrophotometer: switch on the power supply; turn the resistance switch to position '1', then after 5 seconds turn it to position '2', and after a further 5 seconds turn the switch to position '3'. *On no account must the resistance switch be left in position 1 or 2 for longer than 5 seconds.* Switch on the lamps which illuminate the photometer drum e and the wavelength drum i. Open the shutter h and the slits at g and l. If necessary, adjust eyepiece m so that the spectrum is in focus (with a single very thin dark horizontal line across the centre of the field of view). (Adjustment of the telescope at k should not be necessary.) Narrow the eyepiece slit l to a width of about 2 mm, and adjust the intensity of the light by means of the slit at g (the most accurate measurements are made when the intensity is minimal). Set the wavelength drum i at the 5000 Å mark and rotate the extinction drum e by means of the knob f until the upper and lower beams observed through the eyepiece m appear equally intense. Note the reading on the extinction drum. Determine the extinction readings in the same way at 5500, 6000 and 6500 Å. The readings, which are the instrument 'blanks', should be almost independent of wavelength and should not be greater than 0·1.

(c) Fill the absorption cells:

Unscrew one end from a 2-cm absorption cell. With a dropper, fill the cell with the malachite green solution, and gradually slide on the glass end-plate, adding more solution if necessary, so that air bubbles are not trapped. Place the synthetic rubber ring on top of the end-plate and screw on the metal cap *just finger-tight*. In the same way fill the other cell with methanol.

(d) Determine the light absorption curves:

Insert the solution and the solvent cell in the lower and the upper cell-holder respectively. Then determine the E readings for the solution at 100-Å intervals from 5000 to 6500 Å, in the manner already described.

Subtract the 'blank' reading from each of the E readings, convert the corrected E values into ε (see p 172) and plot ε against λ.

Make the measurements on the crystal violet solution similarly, and plot the curve of ε against λ on the same graph. M, malachite green chloride, 365; M, crystal violet chloride, 408.

(*e*) Identify the 'unknown' dyestuff:

Determine the extinction curve of the solution; plot (E/l) against wavelength on the same graph as the other curves. The identity and concentration (c') of the dye can then be deduced.

A good method is to plot (E/cl) for the known dye against (E/l) for the unknown at the same wavelengths. Since the $E_{1\,cm}^{1\%}$ values $(= E/cl)$ at the various wavelengths are characteristic of a compound (i.e. $E_{1\,cm}^{1\%}$ at each wavelength is independent of the individual values of c and l), a straight line plot will be obtained if the dyes are the same, and the slope will give the concentration c' of the 'unknown' solution.

A NOTE ON THE ADJUSTMENT OF THE HILGER–NUTTING VISUAL SPECTROPHOTOMETER

ADJUSTMENT OF THE LAMP AND LENSES

It is assumed that the lamp housing, photometer and prism mounting are already locked in the correct positions on the optical bench and are at the correct height.

(*1*) Remove the collimating lens mounting c. Insert the 'Pointolite' lamp in the holder (a one-position mounting) inside the housing a and adjust the lamp holder so that the tungsten balls lie one behind the other along the main axis of the instrument. Loosen one or both of the screws b_1 and b_2 and adjust the lamp so that the tungsten balls are on a level with the centre of the hole in the lamp housing a, viewed from in front of the photometer e.

(*2*) Replace the lens mounting c and set the holding plate 19·0 cm from the centre of the gap between the tungsten balls of the lamp. Switch on the 'Pointolite' lamp and adjust the height of the lens holder to correspond with the heights of the lenses of the photometer e. The two beams of light should then fall symmetrically on the lenses of e.

(*3*) Remove eyepiece *m*, open shutter *h* and eyepiece slit *l*, set the wavelength drum at *ca*. 6200 Å and open the slit at *g*. Loosen screw b_2, and make a final adjustment to the height of the tungsten lamp so that the two images of one tungsten ball appear one above the other, in the field of view through *m* (without the eyepiece). If the lamp was incorrectly set at (*1*), four images would be seen. (This would be because the tungsten balls were not quite one behind the other along the main axis of the instrument.) If necessary, repeat the adjustments from (*1*). Then rotate the lamp housing *a* very slightly so that the images are centred.

(*4*) Replace the eyepiece *m*, partly close the slit at *g*, narrow the eyepiece slit *l* to about 2 mm and check the instrument blank at several wavelengths (see p 173). If the average reading on the extinction drum is greater than 0·1, the whole series of adjustments should be carefully checked in the correct order, from (*1*).

ADJUSTMENT OF THE SPECTROMETER PRISM

Move the small reflecting prism to the position in front of the slit at *g*, and narrow this slit. Place a sodium lamp behind the instrument at *g* on a level with the small prism. Switch on the sodium lamp.

Open the eyepiece slit *l* and focus the telescope by means of the screw *k*. Set the wavelength drum *i* at 5890 Å. Remove the cover *j* from the spectrometer prism, and adjust the position of the prism until the sodium D-line appears in the centre of the field of view of the eyepiece *m*: check the setting by narrowing the eyepiece slit *l*. Tighten the prism mounting very firmly and carefully replace the prism cover *j*. Finally check the position of the sodium D-line.

Switch off the sodium lamp and swivel the small prism near *g* into its 'resting' position. Switch on the tungsten lamp and focus the telescope by means of the screw *k*. Switch off the tungsten lamp.

29

MEASUREMENT OF REACTION KINETICS

(BY ABSORPTION SPECTROMETRY; PHOTOELECTRIC INSTRUMENT)

INTRODUCTION

MEASUREMENTS of the rates of organic reactions are essential to studies of reaction mechanisms and are useful for the establishment of optimum experimental conditions. In general, physical methods of following reactions are preferable to chemical methods, such as volumetric analysis of a component, because they interfere less with the reacting system, often require smaller quantities of materials and are more readily applicable to *organic* reactions (e.g. molecular rearrangements).

One of the most convenient and versatile physical methods for following organic reactions is absorption spectrometry. The marked changes in ultraviolet or visible light absorption which accompany many reactions of unsaturated compounds can readily be measured even in very dilute solution.

REFERENCES

BRAUDE, *Rep. Progr. Chem.* [*Ann. Reports*], 1945, **42**, 105.
GILLAM and STERN, *Electronic Absorption Spectroscopy*, Edward Arnold (Publishers) Ltd, London, 1954.

DETERMINATION OF RATE CONSTANTS FOR THE ANIONOTROPIC REARRANGEMENT OF PHENYLALLYL ALCOHOL TO CINNAMYL ALCOHOL

(*cf.* BRAUDE, JONES and STERN, *J. chem. Soc.*, **1946**, 396; BRAUDE, *Quart. Rev. chem. Soc., Lond.*, 1950, **4**, 404.)

The reaction $Ph \cdot CH(OH) \cdot CH = CH_2 \rightarrow Ph \cdot CH = CH \cdot CH_2OH$ is accompanied by a large increase in light absorption in the 2500 Å region due to the formation of the cinnamyl alcohol conjugated system.

Prepare the reaction medium in a 100-c.c. standard flask: mix purified dioxane (59·2 c.c.) (refluxed over sodium, fractionated and stored in the dark under nitrogen) with 1·0M-hydrochloric acid

176

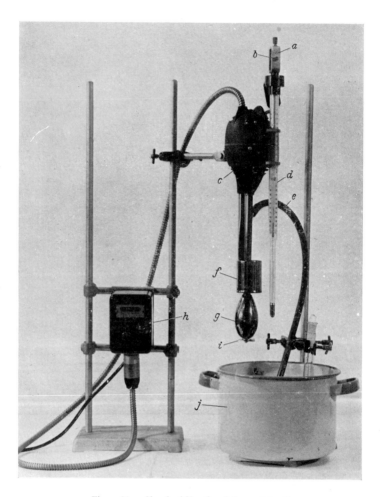

Figure 89.   Shandon 'Circotherm' thermostat unit

(a) *Permanent magnet, rotation of which raises or lowers contact wire* (b) *Locking screw*   (c) *Electric motor*   (d) *Contact thermometer*   (e) *Tubing from pump* (f) *Immersion heater*   (g) *Circulating pump*   (h) *Relay which controls heater* (i) *Stirrer propeller*   (j) *Water-bath*

(10·2 c.c.) and make up the volume to the mark with distilled water. Shake the flask well. An addition of 1·0 c.c. of dioxane to a 50-c.c. portion of this medium (see below) will give a solution accurately 0·1M with respect to hydrogen chloride in 60 per cent by volume aqueous dioxane.

Weigh out accurately (see p 125) about 5 mg of phenylallyl alcohol into a 10-c.c. standard flask, and add purified dioxane to the mark. Mix the solution thoroughly.

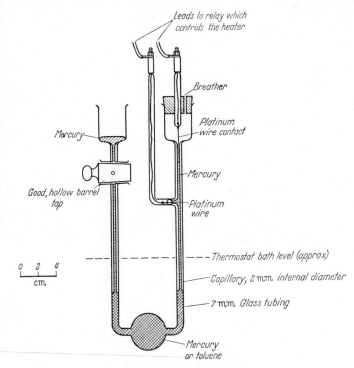

Figure 90. Thermostat regulator

Pipette a 50-c.c. portion of the reaction medium into a 100-c.c. standard flask. Replace the stopper and immerse the flask to the neck in a thermostatically controlled bath set at 50°.

Figure 89 shows a bath (distilled water or oil) and a Shandon 'Circotherm' unit. This consists of a circulating pump and stirrer, and an electric immersion heater regulated by a contact thermometer (range 0–105°) and a relay. *Figure 90* shows another

177

common type of regulator, the bulb of which contains, e.g., mercury or toluene. When the surrounding bath has reached the required temperature, open the tap and tilt the regulator so that the mercury in the right-hand tube just makes contact with the tungsten wire. Close the tap and *then* bring the regulator back to its upright position.

Allow one hour for the solution to reach thermal equilibrium. Then add 1·0 c.c. of the dioxane solution of phenylallyl alcohol, and stopper the flask and shake it vigorously in the thermostatically controlled bath. Note the time. *At once* withdraw a 4·0-c.c. sample with a pipette and run the solution into a weighing bottle containing aqueous 0·5M-sodium acetate (1·0 c.c.), in order to slow down the reaction (*ca.* 1000-fold). Put the cap on the bottle and make the contents homogeneous by careful swirling.

The half-time of the reaction at 50° is about 2 hours. Hence, every 40 minutes, withdraw a sample (4·0 c.c.) until 5 samples have been collected and withdraw a final sample the next morning. Run each sample, at once, into 0·5M-sodium acetate (1·0 c.c.), as before, and note the time. Without delay, determine the extinction (*E*) of each sample at 2510 Å with the Unicam SP. 500 spectrophotometer [Unicam Instruments (Cambridge) Ltd, Cambridge] (see below), using a 1-cm quartz cell: fill the second cell with a 'blank' solution.

Prepare the 'blank' solution as follows. In a 10-c.c. standard flask mix purified dioxane (6·0 c.c.) with 0·1M-hydrochloric acid (1·0 c.c.). Make up the volume to the mark with distilled water, shake the flask and then pipette a 4·0-c.c. portion into aqueous 0·5M-sodium acetate (1·0 c.c.), and mix the solution thoroughly.

The *E* value of the initial reaction sample should be less than 0·1 and that of the final sample should be *ca.* 0·8. Convert the *E* values to ε (see Chapter 28) and calculate values for the first-order rate constant *k* from the equation

$$k = \frac{2\cdot3}{t} \times \log_{10} \frac{\varepsilon_\infty - \varepsilon_0}{\varepsilon_\infty - \varepsilon_x}$$

where t = time in minutes, ε_0 and ε_∞ = initial and final ε values, and ε_x = values at various times.

Tabulate the observations and results as in *Table IV*.

Calculate the mean value for $k^{50°}$.

If time permits, carry out a second run at 60°. The half-time for the rearrangement reaction will now be *ca.* 1 hour, so that a sample should be taken every 20 minutes. From the two values of the rate constants, $k^{50°}$ and $k^{60°}$, calculate the energy of activation **E** for the rearrangement of phenylallyl alcohol, using the equation

$$\ln k_2 - \ln k_1 = (\mathbf{E}/R)(1/T_1 - 1/T_2)$$

where R is the gas constant and T is in ° absolute.

Table IV

t(obs.)	t (calc.)	E	ε_x	$\varepsilon_\infty - \varepsilon_x$	k
0	—	—	—	—	—
1	0	*	ε_0		
40	39	*	*	*	*
80	79	*	*	*	*
.	.	.	.	.	.
.	.	.	.	.	.
.	.	.	.	.	.
1000	∞	*	ε_∞	—	—

INSTRUCTIONS FOR THE UNICAM SPECTROPHOTOMETER
SP. 500 (*Figure 91*)

Light from the source, a hydrogen lamp (ultraviolet) or tungsten lamp (visible), passes through a quartz prism monochromator and then through the solution or solvent on to a photoelectric cell. There are separate photocells (controlled by the knob m) for the regions 2000–6250 Å and 6250–10,000 Å. The amplified photocell output is balanced by means of a slide-wire potentiometer, controlled with the 'density' knob which is calibrated in E and in percentage transmission.

(*1*) Transfer the main plug from the 'Charger On' socket to that marked 'Instrument On'. (By having two sockets and the instrument wired through a 4-pin plug, it is impossible to connect the instrument to the mains and to the charger simultaneously; this is an advisable safeguard.)

(*2*) Switch on the instrument (see *Figure 91*) by turning switch f to 'Check' and switch on the hydrogen lamp by depressing switch a. After 2 minutes press the button b. The ammeter should then read *ca.* 300 mA. (If it does not, switch the hydrogen lamp off at a and seek technical assistance.) Make sure that the lamp lever at k is turned to the right-hand position marked 'H' for the hydrogen lamp.

(*3*) Adjust the sensitivity, if necessary, by turning knob e three turns anticlockwise from its extreme position. (It is convenient to have a cord, part of which is coloured red, attached to the spindle of the knob, so that the red portion is fully wound up when the knob is at the optimum setting.)

(*4*) Remove the lid j from the cell compartment and place it on the instrument at n (NOT on the bench). Lift out the cell carrier.

Rinse one of the quartz cells (1 cm) with the 'blank' solution and then fill it to 1 cm from the top. Similarly fill the other cell with the reaction mixture. Wipe the outsides of the cells with a *soft* cloth, put on the lids and place the cells in the cell carrier in positions p and o with the 'blank' solution at p and the transparent sides of the cells visible through the windows of the carrier. Check that there are no smears on the outsides of the cells by holding the carrier up to the light and looking through the cells. Carefully insert the cell carrier in the cell compartment so that the locating pins fit into the holes in the carrier support.

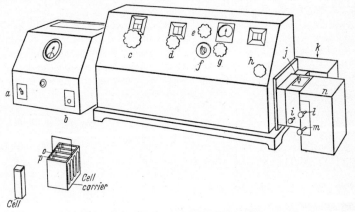

Figure 91. Unicam Spectrophotometer SP. 500

(5) Replace the lid j. Check that knob m is pushed right in.

(6) Zero the galvanometer by turning the dark current control g.

(7) Set the wavelength dial c at 2510 Å.

(8) Pull out the knob l ('dark current') to its full extent.

(9) Zero the galvanometer by turning the slit control h.

(10) Turn the main switch f of the instrument to the '1' position and *at the same time* pull out the cell carrier control i to the first notch.

(11) Zero the galvanometer by turning the transmission density knob d.

(12) Return the cell carrier to its original position by pushing in the knob i and *at the same time* return the switch f to 'Check'.

(13) If the galvanometer does not return to zero, reset the slit (knob h) and repeat from (10).

(*14*) Record the wavelength (on the scale at *c*) and the extinction *E* (on the *lower scale* on the transmission density dial at *d*).

(*15*) Repeat operations (*9*)–(*14*) with each of the other samples in the cell *o*. From time to time check the dark current by pushing in the knob *l*, and, if necessary, zero the galvanometer by turning the dark current control *g*. Repeat (*8*) and continue (*9*)–(*14*).

Then close down the instrument:

(*16*) Push in the knob *l*.

(*17*) Switch off the hydrogen lamp at switch *a*, and the instrument at switch *f*.

(*18*) Return the main plug of the instrument to the 'Charger On' socket.

(*19*) Take off the lid *j* and lift out the cell carrier. Empty the cells, rinse them with ethanol and put them in their box. Return the carrier to the cell compartment and replace the lid *j*.

SUBJECT INDEX

Abbe refractometer, 64
Absorptiometer, Gallenkamp single photocell, 165, 168
   Hilger 'Spekker', 165, 167
Absorption spectrometry, 171–175, 176–181
Absorption spectrophotometer, Hilger–Nutting, 172–175
   adjustment, 174
   Unicam SP. 500, 179–181
Acetone, 107
Acetone dinitrophenylhydrazone, 120
Acetophenone, 162
Acetylene carbinols, 104, 107
Acetylene purification, 106–107
Acetylene, sodio derivative, 106
Active hydrogen estimation, 138–143
   apparatus, 142
Adams's catalyst, 84
Adipic acid, 19
Adsorption chromatography, 3–8
   apparatus, 4, 7
   packing of columns, 3, 5, 6, 7
Air-bath, 44, 148
α-Alanine, 17, 24
β-Alanine, 17
Albumin crystals, 36 *(facing)*
Aldehydes, preparation, 98
Alumina, for chromatography, 3, 6–8
   grading of, 3
Aluminium phosphate catalyst, 101
Amino-acids, detection in eluate, 24
   detection on paper, 17, 21, 35
   identification, 13–17
   ion-exchange chromatography, 22
   ionophoretic separation, 34
   map (two‑dimensional paper chromatogram), 17

Amino-acids, paper chromatography, 13, 20
   test for, 24
p-Aminobenzoic acid, 166
α-Amino-n-butyric acid, 17
α-Amino*iso*butyric acid, 17
β-Amino*iso*butyric acid, 17
γ-Amino-n-butyric acid, 17
α-Amino-octanoic acid, 17
Ammonia, *see* Liquid ammonia
   absorption trap, 102
   determination, 135
   distillation, 136
Ampoules, for liquid specimens, 70, 71–72
   for weighing of liquids, 127
   in Barger method for M, 150
   in Rast method for M, 145
Analysis, ampoules and specimen tubes, 60–62, 70–72
   drying of solids for, 60–62
   purification of liquids for, 63–73
   purification of solids for, 54–62, 50–53
   quantities for, 54
   sealing of liquid samples, 71, 72
Anhydrone, 128, 131, 133
Aniline, hydrogenation, 93
Anisole, for Zerewitinoff reagent, 139
Anodic coupling, 113–115
Anthracene, chromatography, 3
Anti-bumping tube, 67, 68
Arginine, 17
Arsanilic acid, 166
Asparagine, 17
Aspartic acid, 17, 24
Autoclaves, 92, 94
Azobenzene, 150
Azo-dyes, colorimetry, 166

190